SCIENTISTS AND WAR

SCIENTISTS AND WAR

THE IMPACT OF SCIENCE
ON MILITARY AND CIVIL AFFAIRS

SIR SOLLY ZUCKERMAN

HARPER & ROW, PUBLISHERS

New York and Evanston

LIBRARY OF CONGRESS CATALOG CARD NUMBER: 67–11333

B-R

FOR PAUL AND STELLA

Contents

Contents

Preface

THE SEVEN CHAPTERS OF THIS BOOK CONSTITUTE A SERIES OF
related essays which were originally prepared as lectures or addresses. The first four are the Lees Knowles Lectures on Science
and Military Affairs which I delivered, under the auspices of
Trinity College, Cambridge, in October and November of 1965.
Chapter Five, "Priorities and Secrecy in Science," is an edited
version of a Convocation Address which was presented in Washington, D.C., in May, 1966, to the Vicennial Celebrations of
the United States Office of Naval Research, under the title
"The Open World of Science." Chapter Six, "Liberty in the
Age of Science," is a Commencement Address which I gave at
the California Institute of Technology in June of 1959. It was
published at the time, minus some cuts which I have now re-
stored, in Volume 184 of *Nature*. The final chapter of the book,
"The Social Function of Science," is the Rickman Godlee Lecture which I delivered at University College in London in 1960.

Although neither of the last two chapters deals with problems
of defense I have included them in this volume because both
develop in a general context and in greater depth a theme which
I touch on in the first five chapters. This is that there are major
constraints to the freedom with which the goals of scientific and
technological activity can be selected, and that whatever the
goals that may be chosen, their achievement carries the risk of
being associated with unpredictable social repercussions. This
theme is basic to any consideration of the impact of science on

war and on the apparatus of war. The decisions which we make today in fields of science and technology determine the tactics, then the strategy, and finally the politics of tomorrow. In the military field we have only to think of nuclear weapons, and in the civil sphere television, to realize the force of this simple, almost platitudinous, generalization.

The successive steps of the scientific process differ greatly in the nature, in the potential scale and in the imminence of their unknown social consequences. They also imply totally different areas of social and political choice. It is one thing, for example, to decide to use known scientific principles to develop a small nuclear reactor for the specific purpose of propelling a ship at sea. The choice is based on as close an assessment as can be made of the relevant technical possibilities and economic rewards, in comparison with those of other possible schemes in which the same resources of trained manpower and money could be used. However vague the potential consequences of a decision either to go ahead with such a proposition or to drop it, one at least has in mind some kind of outline, in terms of both time and scale, of the possible outcome. But in the case of the particular basic research that resulted in the emergence of the scientific principles which could be put to use in a nuclear reactor, there was at the start no possibility at all of saying what its outcome would be—whether it would be far-reaching scientifically or of no significance at all; whether its application would be useful socially or worthless; and, if applied, whether the application would pass unnoticed or would have a transforming effect on political and economic relations. There was no more possibility of determining these things than there was an element of conscious or external social choice in deciding whether the thought that resulted in the new scientific principles should have been either encouraged or stifled.

The distinction between pure basic research, as a step in the scientific process, and what is definable as applied research, is often blurred. In some fields of science, for example major parts of biology, it has long been realized that there is hardly any distinction at all. But nonetheless it is urgent that the existence of a difference be recognized if the world at large is to appreciate how much, or how little, choice it has in determining its future in this scientific and technological age of ours, and how fast its future is being both set and transformed. I remember, shortly after the end of the Second World War, congratulating one of the top-level nonscientific directors of the Manhattan Project, the name by which the American program to develop the atom bomb was known, on the success of his efforts. With the conversation flagging, I threw in a question about the widely advertised campaign then going on in the United States to raise funds in order to intensify and extend research into the cancer problem. "Do you think," I asked, "that if you personally were furnished with the same powers in administering a search for a cancer cure as you enjoyed in the Manhattan Project the problem would be solved?" "Yes," came the reply, "provided I could stop you scientists wasting time on the things which interest you."

This answer epitomized for me once and for all the confusion which often exists in the minds of people who are not scientists about the nature of the scientific process. King Canute demonstrated that he could not command the tides. What we all need to learn is that the consequences of scientific activity also cannot be commanded, any more than, to use the modern jargon, the layman can command a scientist or technologist to make a "breakthrough" in this or that problem. A cure for cancer will be discovered only when some new genius reaches a new understanding; one day perhaps another genius will discover how to tame the process of nuclear fusion, in the same way as that of fission has been; and in the fullness of time maybe someone will develop a simple and effective device which will allow us to see in the dark. But none of these things will happen except as the spontaneously creative acts of particularly gifted individuals.

These generalizations apply equally in the sphere of defense and in the civil world. But there are major quantitative differences. The volume of national resources which is devoted to the applications of science for military purposes is usually enormous relative to that which governments set aside in the civil sphere. The main reason for this is the arms race, with which I deal in Chapter 2. The limits to which science is "forced" in the military sphere are in the end set by the patience and persuasive powers—and persuasive in several directions—of the men who have the responsibility of seeing that the presumed needs of national security are met. In the civil field the question of what kind of science to promote, or what piece of scientific application to choose, is much more constrained. In the first place, far less money goes to pure basic research than to orientated or objective basic research; and what does become available is subject to fierce competition between contesting claims which are mainly focused on scientific merit as opposed to utilitarian promise. In the nonpublic sector of the economy, an unrelated series of private assessments of the possible market determines what kinds of new scientific knowledge will be selected for development, and how much they are to be supported. Some kinds of developments, for example nuclear energy, are too costly for private enterprise, and the government then has to step in. Since relatively small public financial resources are normally made available for scientific developments which do not have a direct military application, the choice of which to select for support is much influenced by pressure groups, each with a different vested interest in its own field of technology, and all applying their persuasive powers wherever they find it appropriate. Ultimately, in such cases, the decision must be political. These are matters with which I deal in Chapter 5.

In spite of this observation, and even though the scientist or engineer himself cannot foretell the social and political repercussions of his discoveries or developments, it has always been my view, as will appear from the pages which follow, that the scientist has a special responsibility, in both the military and civil fields, in the process of deciding what science should be encouraged and what science applied. I say this because the scientist's knowledge of the basic facts whose application is

determining the increasing complexity of our industrial civilization is intrinsic, and not derivative. However little he may know
of the outcome, he knows more about the problems that may be
involved than does any "gifted amateur." Looking from within
at the hazy coastline which fringes the limits of scientific knowledge, he always has reason to hope that the direction into which
he is peering might one day become illuminated with new
understanding. Not so for the layman. When he gazes from
outside upon the body of science and technology, only too often
does he see reflections of his own wishful thoughts.

The views and ideas which appear in this book are my own,
and the responsibility for ventilating them is also mine, although
as a public servant I had to seek formal permission before
publishing them. What I say does not necessarily reflect the
views of Her Majesty's Government.

References, as well as a series of notes designed both to bring
Chapters 6 and 7 up to date and to amplify some points in my
recent Lees Knowles lectures, are provided at the end of the
book. A few technical terms are explained as footnotes.

Needless to say, critical comments from a number of colleagues, who are too many to name, have helped shape my views
over the years, and to all of them I am grateful. But I should like
to acknowledge publicly my debt to two members of my staff—
Dr. I. J. Shaw and Mr. E. A. Lovell—who were always ready to
check both my facts and my references. It is a great sadness to
me that Mr. Lovell was tragically killed before I was able to
show him my Lees Knowles Lectures in their final shape.

I should like to take this opportunity of expressing my appreciation of the high honor paid me by the Master and Fellows
of Trinity College, Cambridge, in inviting me to give the 1965
Lees Knowles lectures; by the President and Trustees of the
California Institute of Technology in selecting me as their
Commencement Speaker in 1959; by the Provost and authorities
of University College, London, in appointing me Rickman Godlee Lecturer in 1960; and by the U.S. Office of Naval Research

in charging me with the pleasant task of delivering a Convocation Address at its 1966 celebrations. I should also like to acknowledge the kindness of Macmillan and Company for allowing me to reprint the article which they published in *Nature* in 1959.

PART I

Science and Military Affairs

1

An Uneasy Alliance

ALTHOUGH THE GENERALIZATION THAT SCIENCE EXERTS A VITAL influence on political and social relations has a long and venerable history, it did not become popular currency until the Second World War, when Pandora's box opened to reveal to the world the richest store of technological wonders it had ever seen. Not surprisingly, the claim that science is the major transforming force of our times is now heard more insistently in the military world than anywhere else. Atom bombs, radar, supersonic aircraft and ballistic missiles, with the kaleidoscopic effects they have had on international affairs, are reflections of only the most conspicuous facet of the story of the relation of science to military power. Synthetic antimalarial drugs, modern chemical pesticides, herbicides and antibiotics are glimpses of another and more hidden aspect. The effect on the economy of the "military-industrial complex" of applied science, commerce and the military—about which General Eisenhower warned in the valedictory address he delivered as President of the United States—points to a third.[1]* And the impact of scientific method on military affairs is a reflection of a fourth.

They all illustrate the theme that the closest possible connection exists, and will always exist, between science and military affairs. There is nothing startling or controversial about this idea. But because it has always been taken for granted, few have wished to explore it in detail, with the consequence that it has

* Superior numbers refer to Notes and References, page 161.

often been misunderstood or oversimplified. Scientists have been
blamed for the evils of war; and, conversely, there is a belief that
war, or the threat of war, automatically stimulates the growth of
scientific knowledge, just as the sex ratio is said to move in
favor of male births in periods of national stress.[2] If this were
the essence of the story, the aim of this series of essays would be
easily fulfilled. But it is not. Part of my purpose will, therefore,
be to try to disentangle from the relationship which has always
existed between the growth of natural knowledge on the one
hand, and the structure of our social, political and military
institutions on the other, the influence which applied science
has had on the development of weapons of destruction. I shall
also have to explore the relation of technical developments in
the military field to the operational problems of both the soldier
and the politician. In this first chapter I propose to deal mainly
with the somewhat ambivalent relationship that still exists between the soldier and the scientist.

The Roots

The interconnection of science and military affairs long ante-
dates the emergence of organized science as a system of knowledge that has to be deliberately cultivated and exploited. In the
half million years of his existence, man has always hunted and
has always fought; and over the thousands of years that have
passed since the Mesolithic era, when human beings started
their social existence in villages and began the rudiments of
agriculture and trade, there must have been men who, exploiting
and developing the technical skills they inherited, specialized in
the manufacture of stone and metal weapons. The scrap heaps
of prehistoric flint-making sites bear witness to this earliest phase
in the making of armaments. We move on in time. The Bible
tells us of slings and arrows, and of fearsome wars. Greek and
Roman history provides its examples. One of the more romantic
is that of Archimedes, who, in spite of a preoccupation with
mathematical research, and notwithstanding the low regard in

which he, following Plato, is said to have held mechanical contrivances derived from the exploitation of pure science, nonetheless designed fortifications and many engines of war, including a giant catapult, in order to help Hiero keep at bay the Romans who were besieging Syracuse in the latter part of the third century B.C.[3]

When firearms were introduced in the fourteenth century, countless gunsmiths must have busied themselves in improving the accuracy, destructiveness and rate of fire of weapons, and with improving the design of the personal armor worn by warriors. Wherever we look at the contrivances of the fighting men of the Middle Ages, we can see the hand of the emerging scientist and engineer, as well as that of the creative artist, for in those days all art and knowledge were part and parcel of an undivided culture.

Leonardo da Vinci, whose genius filled the latter half of the fifteenth century and beginning of the sixteenth, lives for us in his paintings and drawings. But he was equally one of the great scientists, and probably the greatest mechanical engineer and military scientist of his day.[4] The letter which he wrote to Lodovico Sforza, the ruler of the principality of Milan, offering to provide any instruments of war which he could desire—military bridges, mortars, mines, chariots, catapults and "other machines of marvelous efficacy not in common use"—was the sort of offer which a later generation might have regarded as emanating from a "merchant of death." Michelangelo, whom we know as the greatest sculptor of the Renaissance and the painter of the Sistine Chapel, was at one moment of his career engineer in chief of the fortifications of Florence. English history does not tell of such versatility of contemporary Englishmen, but it does of the early specialization of the profession of armorer. The office of Master of the King's Ordnance, later to be Master General, was established as early as 1414, with a workshop in the Tower of London, where the King's artificers followed their skilled trades. It was here that guns were being made, using all the metallurgical knowledge of the day, as early

as the first half of the fourteenth century.[5] This was the start of
the British Ordnance Board, which still continues, although
with a different postal address. And the Master General still
goes on, although he is no longer President of the Board; nor
does he enjoy—as he did until the year 1828—a seat in the
Cabinet.

The emerging scientists and engineers of the Renaissance
were, of course, involved with far more than just armor and
firearms. Stimulated by the needs of their political masters and
military leaders, craftsmen and scholars concerned themselves
with devices to aid navigation, and with signaling systems like
the heliograph and semaphore. And so it must have gone on
until relatively recent times, over that long period of human
history when it was not beyond the wit of the cultivated man,
whether scholar or artist, professional politician or soldier, to
savor the whole sweep of natural knowledge, and to realize how
that knowledge could be put to work in the furtherance of
material ends.[6] Over the whole of this period, the apparatus and
tactics of armed conflict seem always to have taken full advantage of whatever fruits of science craft industry could exploit.

The Emergence of the Professional Military Man

The age of specialization, ushered in by the industrial revolution, ended all this. From about the time of the Battle of
Waterloo, a kind of divorce seems to have taken place between
the scientist and the soldier, and between science and military
affairs. For all practical purposes the separation endured until
the outbreak of the First World War a century later. During this
long period the military grew into an increasingly potent, prominent and professional social force, at the same time as scientists
started to develop as a race apart, interested, so it seemed to the
lay world, only in new discoveries and new explanations. The
soldier cocooned himself in an isolated and proud professionalism, whose ritual was the admiration of all. The scientist,
groping for new knowledge charged with the power of change,

and the engineer, with his search for new machines and new ways of building things, became enemies of the conventional and established. A real dichotomy of outlook developed over this long period between the fighting soldier on the one hand and his technical colleagues on the other.

This dichotomy led to a strange obtuseness about technical matters on the part of the "general service officer." Examples are endless. Nelsonian tactics continued as formal naval teaching long after they had ceased to be relevant to the weapons of the day. The suggested introduction of steam in the early part of the last century inspired Lord Melville, then the First Lord of the British Admiralty, to write that "their Lordships feel it their bounden duty to discourage to the utmost the employment of steam vessels, as they consider the introduction of steam is calculated to strike a fatal blow to the naval supremacy of the Empire."[7] For years and years iron-clad and powerfully engined men-of-war continued to be furnished with sail. There is a story of one distinguished admiral who never allowed his steam-powered flagship to move except under sail; for all he cared, his engines were just an unnecessary luxury imposed on him by Their Lordships. In 1881 he suffered a stroke. When this happened, his ship was in the doldrums, and his captain was too terrified to start the engines. So he arranged for the ship to be towed to port by other steam vessels of the fleet—until the wise old sea dog realized that in the absence of wind they were moving too fast, and put an end to his captain's ruse.[8]

Many also remember that in spite of the military uses to which balloons had been put on the battlefield for almost a century, army authorities until nearly the beginning of the First World War ruled that there was no military value to aircraft. Marshal Foch, the French military leader of the First World War, expressed his contempt for aviation in the phrase "*tout ça c'est du sport.*"[9] When the French early in the First World War decided to abandon monoplanes in favor of fast biplanes, *Scientific American*,[10] in an article by Ladislas d'Orcy, stated: "This decision, which practically spells the death knell of the monoplane as a military instrument, has not come altogether unexpectedly. Since the beginning of the Great War a number of military airmen openly expressed their opinion about the small value of the monoplane for warfare. The principal arguments that were set forth in this connection were (i) the monoplane's limited carrying capacity, (ii) its limited range of vision, and (iii) its low range of speed." How soon all this was proved to be wrong, and how wrong it was proved to be!

The fight which was still going on thirty years ago to prevent the disappearance of the army horse in an age of fast mechanical propulsion is yet another example of the difficulties that have had to be faced in bringing the potential of modern technology and science to bear on military affairs.

The Contrast of the Scientific and Military Minds

I see two lines of explanation for these illustrations of an obtuseness that must have derived at least in part from a divorce of the military establishment from the advancing fronts of science and technology, a divorce which, as I have said, can be seen as starting about the time the industrial revolution was getting into its stride, and which lasted until about the time of the First World War. If I paint them in strokes which may seem too bold, I do so only in order to help in an understanding of a real problem, and one that has not yet vanished completely from view.

The first is that the unsteady state which science, and the exploitation of science through technology, has always implied, and will always imply, is not compatible with military organization. Nothing is enduring in the scientific world; nothing is sacred. The accelerating rate at which science and technology grow is one of the most outstanding features of our time. Science fits unhappily, if at all, into conventional molds.

The situation is totally different on the military front. However much the armed forces might wish to adjust to changing technological trends, the essence of any military institution is law and order. It is the military man, when it comes to battle, who has the authority to send men to their deaths.[11] Without this authority, armies would be little better than an uncoordinated rabble. The maintenance of authority implies both the pervasive quality of leadership and a stern sense of obedience, which only a powerful discipline can impose. Where it is the habit of the scientist to question, it is that of the soldier to obey. Only those who have belonged to the armed services in the field, or have worked with them, can appreciate just how vital this power of command and authority is to the whole hierarchy of military organization. The soldier learns to accept facts as they are stated; in the words of Tennyson: "Theirs not to reason why, theirs but to do and die."

Discipline of this kind would be impossible in an organization which was subject to the doubts brought about by rapid change, and particularly by the winds of technological change. This is true of the military machine in peace as well as in war. Each level of command accepts the wisdom and the authority of the one above. The soldier must have faith in his weapons. Someone, somehow, must make "the man at the sharp end" believe that the weapons with which he has been provided are at least as good as those the enemy, or potential enemy, has at his disposal. This world of faith and belief, of service loyalty and discipline, is the very antithesis of the one in which science thrives.

My second explanation for the way the military establishment became divorced from the scientific and technological tide which gathered so much force in the nineteenth century relates on the one hand to the isolated professionalism of the services, and on the other to a pervasive social attitude about the place of science and technology in the scheme of things.

For the officer class the profession of arms was always a gentleman's calling. The technologist, as has been impressed on us so often over recent years, has never enjoyed much social prestige—at any rate not in England. Nor, until recently, has the scientist.

I have already mentioned that even as early as the end of the third century B.C., Archimedes, following the precepts of Plato, accorded a much higher prestige value to pure science than he did to the contrivances and machines of war which were based upon its exploitation. Whether this was, in fact, his real attitude, I do not know; the story may merely reflect the prejudice of Plutarch, his first historian, and of other historians who have written about him. But whatever happened in ancient Syracuse, it is the case that in keeping with the trends of Platonic teaching, pure science, with mathematics as the "Queen of the Sciences," has usually been given a higher social rating in the United Kingdom than has any branch of applied science. Neither has been rated as highly as the classics or the humanities. Thomas Arnold's belief in Plato's message, his disdain for useful knowledge and his influence during the nineteenth century on the structure of school education played no little part in bringing about this state of affairs. And it was one which was to endure right into our day. Rutherford, who turned the Cavendish Laboratory into the cradle of nuclear physics, is often quoted as having said that his interests were purely scientific, and that he did not believe that his researches into the nature of the atom could have any practical application.[12] He was one of many who seemed to believe, and who still behave as though they believe, that the intellectual challenge of basic science is incomparably greater and more dignified than that of formulating and overcoming the problems of applied science.

While this attitude is still anything but rare, I am among those who have never believed that there has been any substance to the claim that some kinds of science have a greater purity or intellectual merit than others.[13]

There can be no primary reason for supposing that any one kind of research is intellectually more exacting than any other. It all depends on the quality and interests of the man. In an article called "Anglo-Saxon Attitudes," Sir Peter Medawar[14] has recently given an account of what he regards as various popular conceptions and misconceptions of the scientific process of thought. He begins by reminding us that in England it was Francis Bacon who first made the distinction between basic and applied science, the former increasing our understanding of nature, and the latter our power over it. He then goes on to say that the notion of *purity* has somehow been superimposed upon the concept of a distinction between two kinds of science—"a conscious and inexplicably self-righteous disengagement from the pressures of necessity and use." As he puts it, "the distinction is now rather between polite and rude learning, between the laudably useless and the vulgarly applied, the free and the intellectually compromised, the poetic and the mundane." And he holds that it is only a British, or Anglo-Saxon, vice to accord a higher virtue to the pure as opposed to the applied sciences. "There is a very English thing about making pure and applied science the basis of a class distinction—it helps us forget, perhaps, that it was to our engineers and merchants that we were indebted for that topmost place in the world from which we have now stepped down."

Dancy[15] has given much the same view in a recent address on "Technology in a Liberal Education." He tells us that Plato bit more deeply into English culture, with a resultant prejudice against technology, than into that of France and Germany, where he was read just as widely. And like Medawar, he also sees a reflection of "class" in our attitudes. "Plato was social and intellectual snob rolled into one, a combination irresistible to the English. *His* intellectual theory matched and reinforced *our* traditional practice."

There is no need for me to follow this analysis further in order to make my point. The gulf between the military hierarchy and the world of science, and particularly the world of applied science, which persisted until relatively recently, was in a major sense a reflection of an attitude which existed in society as a whole, and even within science itself. We all seem to have been brought up to believe that different kinds of scientific activity can be graded socially because of a presumption that some imply a higher intellectual quality than others. Parts of the debate stimulated by C. P. Snow's[16] concept of "Two Cultures" seem to reflect this deep-seated attitude.

But if, in their disregard for fruitful and profitable technology,

some of our nineteenth-century soldiers and sailors were merely
following the example of their fellow citizens, including the pure
scientists, one might well ask how it is that it is not only the
British military who have always been accused of always prepar-
ing for the last, as opposed to the next, war. It has always been
for the political power to decide when and for what purposes the
threat of force should be used in the pursuit of political goals.
But such decisions were taken on the basis of professional
military advice, and until recent times politicians were usually
content to leave the intimate, and even broad, details of military
affairs in the hands of their generals and admirals. This stopped
about the time of the First World War. The observation of
Clemenceau, then the French Prime Minister, that war is too
serious to be left to the generals has never ceased to echo around
the world. He may not have been the first to query the innate
wisdom of the military hierarchy, but he was presumably talking
about French as well as British generals. Perhaps, therefore, it is
to the professionalism and isolation of the military establishment in all countries, and not in England alone, that we have to
look more than anywhere else in order to understand the fact
that until quite recent times the military man has been suspicious of the changes which are provoked by technological advance—and correspondingly suspicious of scientists.

The Period of Transition

The First World War was the period of transition in the
relation of the world of science to the military hierarchy. There
had, of course, always been men in the technical branches of the
services, working in such fields as ballistics, hydrography and
surveying. Many of these had become distinguished scientists or
engineers in their own right. But they always constituted a class
of officer separate from those who became members of the
"general staff," and who by so doing got themselves on the
ladder which led to the top. This kind of separation between
specialist and general-duty officer prevails to this very day in
most of the navies, armies and air forces of the world.

The First World War was a turning point because it saw the emergence of submarine warfare, of aircraft and of tanks, and of a vast range of new medical problems which were generated by the horrible conditions under which millions of men lived, fought and died in France and Flanders. The transition in the relationship of science to the military hierarchy was also powerfully influenced by the intrusion into the military machine of the outside scientist and engineer, men like Tizard and Lindemann, to mention two whose names have unfortunately become celebrated less for their achievements as scientists than for dramatic —and disputed—accounts of their personal differences.[17]

Scores of scientists became engaged in the technical backing of the armed services in the First World War. This was the period when aeronautical science was truly born, when men like G. P. Thomson and Aston, in addition to Farren and Lindemann, reinforced the Royal Aircraft Factory at Farnborough, and learned to fly themselves; when the properties of sound and shock waves in water were systematically explored and exploited; and when Lewis'[18] work gave us a new understanding of disorders of the action of the heart.

But the mobilization of scientists as scientists was anything but complete in the First World War. Some of the most brilliant young men of the day were among those who died in battle. When the young atomic physicist Moseley was killed in action in the Dardanelles, Rutherford wrote:[19]

It is a national tragedy that our military organization at the start was so inelastic as to be unable, with a few exceptions, to utilize the offers of services of our scientific men except as combatants in the firing line. Our regret for the untimely end of Moseley is all the more poignant that we cannot but recognize that his services would have been far more useful to his country in one of the numerous fields of scientific inquiry rendered necessary by the war than by exposure to the chances of a Turkish bullet.

The involvement of scientists in the defense effort of Great Britain not unnaturally dwindled in the twenties, but in the thirties, as the signs of an impending European clash became

more and more unmistakable, a countercurrent developed, and
with it a change in the direction of the relationship betweeen
scientist and soldier. Instead of standing by to provide for the
physical needs of the military as the latter saw them, the
scientist began to suggest what these needs were, or at least to
show how scientific knowledge could be usefully exploited
through technology for military ends. In 1934 the then Secretary
of State for Air set up a committee of scientists under Sir Henry
Tizard's chairmanship to advise how air attacks could be countered. One of the first matters which it investigated was the so-
called death ray—a problem which was turned over to Mr. (later
Sir Robert) Watson-Watt, who was then Superintendent of the
Radio Department of the National Physical Laboratory. As the
official history[20] on the subject says:

The committee was probably not deeply impressed by the possibilities
of the death ray, but it was interested to have some figures of the
amounts of electromagnetic energy which might be involved. Mr.
Watson-Watt had had no difficulty in producing figures which
relegated the death ray itself once again to the realm of fantasy, but
having done so he made the countersuggestion that it might be
possible to detect aircraft by radio waves. At the committee's invita-
tion Mr. Watson-Watt pursued this idea in a second paper on the
"Detection and Location of Aircraft by Radio Methods." In this celebrated paper he set out the principles upon which the technique of
radar is based.

Had Watson-Watt stuck to the terms of reference he was
given, it is conceivable that radar would never have been developed in time. And without radar the war would have as-
suredly been lost.

The same kind of independent influence was demonstrated
when Peierls and Frisch, two refugee scientists then working in
association with Professor Oliphant in Birmingham, showed
that it was possible to exploit the process of nuclear fission in the
development of a bomb with a destructive force far beyond
anything man had ever conceived of. There was no staff requirement for such a weapon, and when the attention of the Prime

Minister, Mr. Winston Churchill, was drawn to this advice, he is recorded[21] as having remarked that personally he was quite content with the available power of chemical explosives, but that nonetheless he felt that he "must not stand in the path of improvement." As Margaret Gowing points out in her official history,[22] a remarkable feature of the paper which Peierls and Frisch produced in 1940 is that it not only suggested how U-235 might be separated, but also set out the theoretical reasoning for the critical size of an atom bomb, and showed how it could be detonated, as well as indicating that the effects of radiation would transform the process of warfare. Five years before the first weapon was even exploded experimentally, Peierls and Frisch had pointed out that effective protection against nuclear weapons is hardly possible.

All this represented a major change in the polarity of the relationship between science and military affairs, and to a certain extent a return to the social environment which preceded the age of scientific specialization and the emergence of organized technology—a return to the age when a Leonardo da Vinci could peddle military devices for which neither his political master nor the latter's military advisers could have realized the need, let alone provided the means.

The Birth of Operational Research

With the outbreak of the Second World War, yet another transformation occurred in the affairs of scientists and military men. Instead of limiting himself to the development of advanced equipment, the scientist also started to busy himself with operational matters, and to advise the soldier about the way operational problems should be formulated. This was the origin of what came to be called operational research, or operational analysis—a subject which has flowered in somewhat unexpected fashion, particularly since the electronic computer has provided the means of testing mathematically any complex situation, real or unreal, that can be set out in quantitative terms. But operational research, too, turns out to be an old idea which had simply disappeared from view.

There are those who see in the groups of philosophers whom Alexander the Great[23] got to accompany him on his campaigns, to comment on the way things went, as well as to engage him in enlightened conversation, the precursors of today's operational-research workers. Nearly two thousand years after Alexander's days, Newton[24] wrote that "if instead of sending the Observations of Seamen to able Mathematicians at Land, the Land would send able Mathematicians to Sea, it would signify much more to the improvement of Navigation and Safety of Men's lives and estates on that element."

But Newton's exhortation for the scientifically trained man to be put into the field to study what happened in action had little, if any, effect, for almost 250 years. As recently as 1937, B. H. Liddell Hart[25] was able to write: "The way that decisions are reached on questions of strategy, tactics, organization, etc., is lamentably unscientific. . . . There are no means for the comprehensive analysis of past experience and thus no synthesis of adequately established data to serve as a guide in framing policy."

In the American Civil War, in the Franco-Prussian War, in the First World War, war—in the words of Colonel Nathan Forrest—was still largely a matter of getting there "fustest with the mostest." Fire power had increased over the years both in range and in the degree of physical destruction that could be caused. The tank had increased the possibilities of mobility in the face of enemy fire. Chemical warfare, in spite of its limitations, was a clear-cut and understandable procedure that nearly broke the static conditions of trench warfare. In general, the strategists and tacticians of the First World War were still operating with weapons they could understand over ranges they could, in effect, see, and in accordance with the hallowed military principle of the economy of force.

With one minor qualification, the First World War was thus historically still a period of balanced military forces and balanced weapons systems. The balance lay essentially in the control the commander could exercise over his troops and weapons, the consequences of whose use were also within his comprehension, and potentially, therefore, within his control. I can see no other possible useful meaning to the term "balanced military force."

My one qualification to this generalization was the emergence of air warfare. This was the germ which destroyed the traditional frame in which the military commander had hitherto exercised his judgment and control. Out of the first aircraft grew a weapons system whose striking power was to leap well ahead of the capacity to apply destructive force specifically for the elimination of what it is still both useful and wise to call "military targets." The aircraft was thus as much a leap into the dark as into the air.

In comparison, the submarine, when it first appeared, was a weapon whose effects could be envisaged without difficulty. Submarines certainly imposed a new threat, but it was one which was understandable and technically manageable, given a detection system, depth charges and the intelligent deployment of surface shipping and antisubmarine forces. In its traditional sense, it was—I use the word "was" deliberately, for it is different now that submarines have become launching platforms for ballistic missiles—a weapon system which was posed against specific but mobile targets. The aircraft was something quite different. Able to penetrate deeply into enemy territory, it could achieve effects the consequences of which were unpredictable, and certainly outside the framework of the airman's experience.

The situation started to be remedied before the outbreak of the Second World War in 1939 as a result of the development of radar. "Operational research" emerged as a new procedure in military affairs, as an intellectual tool for the military, so as to help the proper exercise of judgment and control. Without it, warfare was already becoming too difficult technically for those in whose hands its conduct rested. I say this with no disrespect. When he introduced the new discipline into the British military sphere, as a necessary corollary to the development of radar from a laboratory phenomenon to the sensory system on which a modern air force relies, Sir Robert Watson-Watt[26] had in mind: "The application of the basic scientific methods of measurement, classification, comparison and correlation, to the selection of means for attaining, with the least expenditure in effort and in time, the maximum operational effect which could be extracted from the available or potentially available resources in personnel and material."

The primary purpose of operational research when it started at Fighter Command and in other Royal Air Force Commands was to make the best use of the weapons and equipment the United Kingdom had. The fact that the work was done not by the military, who wanted the equipment, but by scientists, of whom few, if any, had had any previous experience of military matters, and many of whom had had no training in the physical sciences which went into the design of weapons, was a measure of the failure of an educational system to train officers to understand either the scientific basis of their weapons and weapon systems or the value of the methods of science. This defect in our educational system has not yet been fully overcome.

Basically, operational analysis implies a kind of scientific natural history. It is a search for exact information as a foundation for extrapolation and prediction. It is not so much a science in the sense of a corpus of exact knowledge, as it is the attempted application of rigorous methods of scientific method and action to new and apparently unique situations. The less exact the information available for analysis, the less it is founded on experience, the more imprecise are its conclusions, however sophisticated and glamorous the mathematics with which the analysis is done.

The technical and tactical area to which operational research applies is defined by the "terms of reference" suggested by Sir Robert Watson-Watt[27]—"to examine quantitatively whether the user organization is getting from the operation of its equipment the best attainable contribution to its over-all objective, what are the predominant factors governing the results attained, what changes in equipment or method can be reasonably expected to improve these results at a minimal cost in effort and in time, and the degree to which variations in the tactical objectives are likely to contribute to a more economical and timely attainment of the over-all strategic objective." Most operational research in the Second World War could be properly classified under these terms of reference.[28]

At the technical level, operational research is mainly concerned with the technical description of agreed operational needs, leading to design studies. The reason why operational research is essential at this level is that it is only when a new weapon—using the term in its broadest possible sense—is under design that the broad lines of its impact on other weapon systems, and on tactical problems in general, can first be theoretically assessed. It is at this stage, more than at any other, that it becomes necessary to consider the resources which the new project will demand. In building a house, one does not spend all one's money on the walls. In designing a weapon, it is absolutely necessary to consider its presumed effects in relation to the diversion of resources which its development and production will demand. There is a further point. In the technological battle between the offensive and defensive, a great deal of work on weapon systems focuses on small marginal developments and improvements. Here, too, is a field for operational research—to see whether the technological effort involved is disproportionately large or small in relation to the importance of the operational requirements which the research effort is trying to meet, and also to determine whether the available technical effort itself is properly balanced between various projects.

Operational research at the tactical level demonstrated its value during the Second World War by providing real information about what happened in operations, so that changes in tactics could be introduced on the basis of fact, and not that of fancy. When confronted with a problem in the tactical sphere, the operational-research worker has always to be alert to the possible defects of anecdotal information that comes from the field. The critical point to realize is that no weapon or weapon system can be properly tested in theory. Weapons can be evaluated only through an analysis of actual operations. And what happens in an operation is not necessarily what is reported by those who took part in it. For example, most of the bombing plans which were prepared at the beginning of the Second World War for the Royal Air Force were characterized by a failure to appreciate the technical and operational limitations which existed at the time. "Not only were the effects of the explosion of relatively small bombs exaggerated and, *pari passu*, the resistance of targets depreciated; the plans were also colored by optimistic views about the capacity of aircraft to find distant targets without the help of special navigational aids, and about the bombing accuracy which could be achieved under operational conditions." As a result of the unrealistic technical and operational background, estimates of the strength which would be required to deal with targets were almost inevitably so optimistic as to be all but worthless.[29]

After real information on these matters had started to pour in, mainly as a result of the work of those scientists who formed the first "operational-analysis units," and after it became possible to plan on a more factual basis, a new difficulty arose. During my own wartime association with the professional planners, I always found it impossible to understand what they meant by a special kind of "operational factor" which they sometimes introduced into the planning picture after realistic calculations had been made of the effort necessary to achieve a particular task—say, a bombing operation. These newer calculations had taken account of the effects of individual bombs, of bombing errors, of errors in navigational and bombing aids—all of which had been determined by dispassionate research into actual experience—and also made allowances for abortive sorties as given by an analysis of previous operations. They also took account of the results of studies which related the physical picture of the destruction of towns and cities to intelligence estimates of falls in industrial production, dislocation of movement by rail and road, and so on. In short, the calculations took account of all such factors as objective study could show were necessary to explain the measurable results of bomber operations in relation to what was intended. Yet, after all these calculations were made, and for some reason which was never defined, it was my experience that the planners often multiplied the answer by a mystical "operational factor," which somehow or other usually turned out to be 2, in order to make allowances for undefined variables which, it was assumed, had not been considered. It was useless explaining that the factors which had been included in the calculations were in themselves sufficient to account for past performance, and that there was no need to double the answer in order to take account of others which no one could even formulate.

A third category of operational research consisted in the analysis of the way military plans—both strategic and tactical—unfolded in actuality, as opposed to how they were supposed to work. It was this kind of operational analysis which I was particularly interested in, and which I had the opportunity to develop as a result of my association first with Admiral of the Fleet Lord Mountbatten, at that time Chief of Combined Operations in the United Kingdom; later with Air Chief Marshal Tedder and Generals Spaatz and Norstad in the Mediterranean Theater; and afterward with Air Chief Marshal Tedder and General Eisenhower, the Supreme Commander of SHAEF from 1944 till the end of the war.

No opportunity of analyzing operations in relation to their stated purpose was afforded us until early 1943, when the Axis forces were driven out of the Western Desert and North Africa. As the British armies advanced, studies were made of Tripoli and of other targets of air operations. The bomb damage as seen on the ground, and as recorded by the civil authorities at the time, was compared with the operational planning of, and intelligence reports on, the attacks which had caused the damage.

Essentially, what was being done was to treat each operation as one might an experiment of a very crude kind. How closely did what was achieved correspond to what we had set out to do?

Why were intention and effect not always the same? A much more direct experimental approach was followed in planning and in executing the operations which led to the capture of the island of Pantelleria in 1943 and in analyzing them afterward—work in which I was closely associated with General Norstad. The lessons learned from this operation were then applied in 1944 to the pre–D Day offensive against the coastal defenses of northern France. Similarly, the lessons learned from a detailed analysis of the functional effects of attacks on the railway system of Sicily and southern Italy provided the rationale for the 1944 plan to destroy the railway network of Northwest Europe with the object not only of dislocating military movement, but also of disrupting the flow of goods and materials, and so of bringing German industrial activity to a standstill. The main objectives of the bombing policies with which this new plan was in conflict had been the destruction of centers of population and industry inside Germany. Analyses of a variety of facts derived from many sources have made it clear to the proponents of the new policy that the overall effects on Germany's war effort of the former offensive were considerably less rewarding per unit of effort than they were in the latter. Subsequent analyses fully confirmed the expectations that had been based on the experience gained in the Mediterranean Theater, experience which was not accepted without a struggle by those strategists and planners who, as a guide to decision, preferred intuition rather than the methods of science.[30]

There was little opportunity for this kind of analysis of field warfare—largely, I think, because it moved too fast for the results, when they became available, to be applied; also, the situations in field warfare were infinitely more varied than in either air or sea war.

Operational Research Today

Toward the end of the Second World War a new type of operational research emerged which involved the evaluation of weapon systems and tactics before they had been tried out in practice. This projective type of operational research, which is not based on the analysis of what has gone before, has increased greatly in the military sphere over the past twenty years, and particularly with the emergence of computers as aids to study.

In the analysis of new weapon systems, guidance is needed in the predesign stage to decide what features of design are most likely to pay off—weapons are too expensive and the lead time to production too long to permit the old policy of "make and test." For example, a sophisticated air-defense system requires ground radar and associated data-handling systems. It needs command links. And these in turn have to be tied in with the active or passive elements which are deployed to deal with the actual attack.

Obviously, the only thing that matters is: "Can the whole system deal with the attack?" If the strike component of the defense is too slow, it does not matter how efficient the radar system is—and so on. Within the limitations imposed by such factors as range and response time, extent of cover, financial cost and lead time, each part of the whole must be designed for optimum efficiency in order to achieve one end result.

In the case of many weapons, particularly nuclear weapons, empirical tests are, of course, out of the question; the computer has to provide the picture of likely operational effects, the basis of the calculations being such established parameters as can be defined on the basis of real experience—both in and outside the laboratory.

One type of study which falls on the fringe of this class of modern operational research is popularly called "cost-effectiveness" analysis, the purpose of which is to decide which of two or more alternative ways of achieving a given military purpose is the most economic from the point of view of the resources employed. It is not enough merely to compare the costs of developing and producing two or more alternative weapon systems. The comparison must also take in the cost of operating the weapons. Cost-effectiveness studies and comparisons have, therefore, to take into account such factors as maintenance, personnel and transport over the period a weapon system is likely to be in service before it is declared obsolete. The snag about these studies and comparisons is that it is very difficult to define effectiveness in the military sphere, even when one can estimate—which is by no means always—the costs of development or of the operation of the weapon. Cost-effectiveness comparisons need, therefore, to be treated more as a guide to action than as scientific statements. They work well when one is considering, say, the relative costs of two competitive projects for long-range delivery systems of nuclear weapons where both the point of launch or takeoff and the precise location of the target are known. But where one is dealing with the highly changing circumstances of field warfare in which the number of variables are themselves both uncountable and unpredictable, efforts to give a quantitative look to a comparison of weapons can be highly misleading. Nonnumerical objective analysis and judgment based upon experience may in such circumstances be a far more valuable way of dealing with the problem.

Another form which operational research takes today is "scenario analysis"—the postulation of likely situations of conflict, and the study of the possible outcome of various strategies and tactics. In these studies it is necessary to allow for chance variations to a far greater degree than was required in the Second World War, when the repetitive nature of many operations permitted an average result to be used as a criterion for assessment. This new type of analysis demands the use of digital computers to permit the making of a very large number of runs with very large numbers of randomly selected parameters, in order to establish the distribution of possible results and thus the measure of the probability of a given outcome occurring on a particular occasion.

In lieu of something better as a guide to action, scenario analysis, as well as certain forms of theorizing for which members of the modern school of so-called strategic analysts have become responsible, have a real value. But there are types of abstract strategic analysis which, in my view, have to be taken

with more than a grain of salt. I say this even though parts of the
very wide areas with which the calculations of some strategic-
game theorists deal are amenable to rigid treatment by formal
logic, and probability statistics or mathematics, and that the
conclusions which emerge may be valid over the part of the field
to which they relate. What worries me is the fact that the total
situation with which the theorists deal also contains extremely
broad parameters of so qualitative a nature that no one could
attribute numerical values to them. Some of these parameters
are among the most important issues with which one group of
game-theory strategists pretend to deal—if not the most important. For example, they include such matters as the enemy's
intentions, as well as his strength and capacity; the resolution of
our people; the capacity of a country to restore itself economi-
cally when it has suffered a degree of devastation well beyond
anything that lies within human comprehension—let alone experience—and other matters equally vague. These are vitally
important issues. But they are not numerical issues, and probably never could be made such, even if they were ever to come
within our experience. I return to this point in a later chapter.

Mathematical conceptions of probability clearly have real
value in experimental situations when they relate to precise
issues. But the more qualitative and nonnumerical—the more
human—the factors that are played into the system, the less
precise and, indeed, the less meaningful become the estimates of
probability that are churned out of the machine. One has to
remember, too, that the social and political significance and
weight of the different qualitative factors concerned in these
strategic situations vary not only between themselves but also
from moment to moment. Strategy, no more than politics, can
be static.

Before the more eclectic forms of abstract strategic analysis
began to attract attention, Whitehead,[31] the renowned philosopher and mathematician, had written:

There is a curious misconception that somehow the mathematical
mysteries of statistics help us to evade the proper limitations of the

observed past. But statistics tell you nothing about the future unless you make the assumption of the permanence of statistical form. . . . Mathematics can tell you the consequences of your beliefs. For example, if your apple is composed of a finite number of atoms, mathematics will tell you that the number is odd or even. But you must not ask mathematics to provide you with the apple, the atoms and the finiteness of their number. There is no valid inference from mere possibility to matter of fact, or in other words, from mere mathematics to concrete nature.

If ever there was a world in which situations do not repeat themselves like some mass-production model, it is the military world. If we are to avoid the imposition of arbitrary limits to the exercise of judgment and control, we must be careful not to create in a mathematical vacuum situations which are based neither on past experience of affairs, nor on any conception of the innumerable variables and factors that determine social decision either today or tomorrow. The human brain, human values, human judgments, are still superior to the mechanics and processes of electronic computers or guidance systems. The day this ceases to be true, there will probably be no human brains. But until then, true scientific method should be used as an aid to human judgment—and not as a hindrance. Science *is* human experience; it is not an alternative to judgment, and it is certainly not something that can operate outside human experience.

Much of what I have said about operational research applies—and experience has shown with equal force—in other fields of human activity. In the competitive world in which we live, science and technology are as much part of the foundation of industrial power as they are of military power. Speed and economy of operation, no less than the prediction of possible change, necessitate as intimate and as quantitative a knowledge of the way processes unfold in, let us say, the economic and industrial fields as they do in the military. Systems analysis of industrial operations, market research, and so on, are some of the techniques used by the operational-research worker in these nonmilitary fields.

In all of them the aim remains the same. It is that of applying the dispassionate methods of analysis which are used in the scientific world in order to foretell the way events might unfold, given these or those circumstances. It is, of course, unfortunate that the scope for prediction in spheres of economic analysis is very much more confined than in those fields of knowledge where it is possible to apply the methods of the natural sciences. The "stochastic (or random) nature of all economic relationships," as Johnston[32] has put it, "detracts greatly from the value of predictions based upon econometric analyses of model systems." And as another distinguished economist, Professor Samuelson,[33] has recently remarked, "the vision of the best economic forecasters gives out when we talk about periods so far ahead as a year." If such a limitation applied to the scientist, there would, of course, be no science.

In his 1939 Lees Knowles lectures on "Generals and Generalship," the late Field Marshal Lord Wavell[34] remarked that the real foundation of "military knowledge" is knowledge of the "mechanism of war." "It is the lack of this knowledge of the principles and practice of military movement and administration—the 'logistics' of war some people call it—which puts what we call amateur strategists wrong, not the principles of strategy themselves, which can be apprehended in a very short time by any reasonable intelligence." By this observation he implied that tactics could hardly be associated with an ignorance of new military techniques, nor strategy with an unreal conception of what is tactically and administratively possible. He could have added the platitude—not always acted on in practice—that military planning will be the more effective the more it is based on an objective appreciation of the facts with which it is concerned. Whatever its limitations, therefore, the need for operational research, in all its forms, is likely to increase rather than decrease as science and technology extend the area of their influence in military and social affairs. It is no longer possible to conduct the business of politics and statesmanship in slow time. Too many of the problems of present political and military life spring from the bubbling fount of science. As science increas-

ingly becomes the material for politics and military affairs, the
more likely, therefore, is it that they will need to call for the use
of scientific methods of thought. As a result of the recent
reorganization in the British Defense Departments, scientists are
now concerned not only with operational research at the technical and tactical levels, but also in the strategic field. In facing the
challenge which this fact implies, our immediate problem, as
scientists, will be that of not overreaching ourselves. Many of
the speculative exercises which go by the name of systems
analysis and in which computers are used, deal with the analysis
and comparison of complex situations of which assumptions,
as I have indicated, are usually a critical component. Poorly selected assumptions can lead to highly misleading and dangerous
conclusions. The scientist is no witch doctor. His contribution to
forward military thinking will serve a purpose only to the extent
that he uses the advanced techniques which computer technology has made possible in the analysis of situations in which
established facts have a place. And the facts, the real facts, will
not come to him of their own accord. It is for the military
scientist to go out and seek them—in the laboratory, through
field tests and by direct observation in theaters where our forces
might be engaged in active operations. Only in this way will he
be able to submit his assumptions to critical test, at the same
time as he helps transform the anecdotes and wishful thinking
of military lore into the kind of fact for which his military
colleagues are seeking, and without which a government cannot
take wise action.

The Alexanders of today still need their philosophers; and to
be of use, the philosophers have got to see their Alexanders at
work.

2

The Impact of Technology

PRESIDENT EISENHOWER'S VALEDICTORY ADDRESS,[1] TO WHICH I
referred in the preceding essay, provides a useful frame for the
consideration of the interaction of modern technology and military affairs. Its message reverberated round the world, and the
echoes of a passage I wish to quote have not yet died down:

Until the latest of our world conflicts, [said the President] the United
States had no armaments industry. American makers of plowshares
could, with time and as required, make swords as well. But now we
can no longer risk emergency improvisation of national defense; we
have been compelled to create a permanent armaments industry of
vast proportions. Added to this, three and a half million men and
women are directly engaged in the defense establishment. We annually spend on military security more than the net income of all United
States corporations.

This conjunction of an immense military establishment and a large
arms industry is new in the American experience. The total influence—economic, political, even spiritual—is felt in every city, every
state house, every office of the federal government. We recognize the
imperative need for this development. Yet we must not fail to comprehend its grave implications. Our toil, resources and livelihood are
all involved; so is the very structure of our society.

In the councils of government, we must guard against the acquisition of unwarranted influence, whether sought or unsought, by the
military-industrial complex. The potential for the disastrous rise of
misplaced power exists and will persist.

We must never let the weight of this combination endanger our liberties or democratic processes. We should take nothing for granted. Only an alert and knowledgeable citizenry can compel the proper meshing of the huge industrial and military machinery of defense with our peaceful methods and goals, so that security and liberty may prosper together.

It is possible that the departing President was less than fair in this statement to the American armaments industry as it existed in the era before the Second World War. As far back as 1853, the year before the outbreak of the Crimean War, the British government was sufficiently impressed with American performance in the mass production of small arms, with interchangeable parts, to set up a plant at Enfield, Middlesex, to produce rifles and muskets by means of American machine tools. Very soon after, private industry followed suit at Small Heath, Birmingham, and with an output of nearly half a million weapons a year in its first ten years of operation, this plant soon outstripped the performance of the Enfield factory.[2]

The Place of Defense Industry in National Economies

On the other hand, the ex-President's picture of the general position is, if anything, an understatement of what goes on. A recently published official report on the Economic Impact of Defense and Disarmament[3] tells us that American manufacturing and building firms concerned with defense, space and atomic energy, which from the industrial point of view are all related activities, account for about 5 percent of total employment in the United States. When one includes members of the armed forces and the staff of government defense agencies, the figure becomes 10 percent. Over the past decade the armed services and the firms which catered to their needs consumed 85–90 percent of all federal government purchases of goods and services. Government money channeled through the Department of Defense, the National Aeronautics and Space Administration and the Atomic Energy Commission accounts for more than half of the research carried on in industrial laboratories and about three-fifths of the work pursued in universities and corresponding institutions. More than 300,000 professional scientists and engineers are engaged today in this work.

The figures speak for themselves. There can be no doubt that American government money, voted mainly to satisfy the needs of defense, is putting its stamp on the pattern of tomorrow's scientific knowledge, and on the trends of today's technological developments.

In absolute terms, British expenditures are minuscule by comparison, although in terms of the proportion of the Gross National Product* which we spend on defense, we are not far behind.[4] How our own, and American, expenditures compared relatively and absolutely with Russian outlays in a matter for speculation, although it is a fair guess that the United Kingdom is a mere dwarf by comparison. The Russian effort, which in real scale is probably not far behind the American, is also helping to set the pattern and pace for the development of those industries which are based on modern technology—and in particular on the aviation and electronics industries.

The Impact of Civil and Military Technology

From about the time of the Industrial Revolution until the Second World War, the technological needs of the armed forces were, in general, met out of the same scientific and technical knowledge which manufacturing industry had put to use in satisfying commercial demands. The picture became transformed, as I pointed out in the preceding chapter, when scientists, instead of standing back and allowing the military to get on with their own affairs, stepped into the arena with proposals such as those which led to the development of radar and the nuclear bomb. Since then the situation has gone on changing, particularly because of the immense resources that have been

---

* *Gross National Product:* The G.N.P. is a commonly used expression of a country's income. There are different ways of defining and calculating the G.N.P. In nontechnical terms, the G.N.P. may be said to be the aggregate of all output.

made available for defense during the subsequent long period of cold war, with its many eruptions of open conflict, as in Korea and Vietnam.

Unlike civil industry, where the amount of money spent on development projects is determined mainly by social, economic and commercial considerations—by considerations of cost, competition and potential profit—research and development projects in the sphere of defense are in theory limited only by the extremes to which scientific and technical knowledge can be mobilized and pushed, and in practice by the extent to which nations are willing to divert resources from other social and political ends. In the changed relationship between science and military affairs that has prevailed since the Second World War, the military man has never ceased to urge the scientist to intensify the technological exploitation of his knowledge in order to improve the armory of available weapons; and within the economic restraints set them, the scientist and engineer have been only too ready to oblige, to the full extent of their abilities. As a result, the development of established technologies has been accelerated, and new ones have been created. In radar, for example, the particular problems posed by transforming relatively simple scientific apparatus designed for the study of the ionosphere into a range of military equipment capable of finding and tracking enemy aircraft at great ranges, of detecting a submarine snort mast against a background of sea clutter,* of seeing a small target move against a stationary background, has led to the development of totally new valves, of totally new circuit techniques and of totally new theories that are needed to understand the properties of the wanted signals in relation to those of

* Sea clutter: A radar system works by transmitting radio energy and detecting any that is reflected back toward the transmitter. The reflection from the target of interest is often accompanied by reflections from other objects illuminated by the beam which are of no operational significance. These unwanted and often troublesome reflections are referred to as "clutter." Sea clutter—that is, reflection from waves on the surface of the sea—is particularly troublesome in the radar search for submarine snort masts, since the wanted and unwanted signals are of about the same intensity, and are not separated in range.

the unwanted signals or "noise" by which they are invariably accompanied. The guidance techniques called for by ballistic and other missiles have forced the development of gyroscopic engineering to an extent never before dreamed of. The need to pack a lot into a little in order to reduce the size and weight of various kinds of electronic equipment has stimulated the development of solid-state physics* and its practical exploitation in the microminiaturization of components. If the demands of new weapon systems had not provided the spur they have, the technology of servomechanisms† would never have advanced as it has. In the field of nuclear technology, processes which had been understood in university laboratories had to be scaled up thousands of times, sometimes in the face of unforeseen and formidable engineering difficulties, and put to work, for example, in gigantic gaseous-diffusion plants. A new branch of chemical engineering capable of handling dangerous radioactive materials had to be developed. And metals which hitherto were only scientific curiosities had to be studied until their chemistry and metallurgy were as well understood as those of copper and iron.

The Sophistication of Weapons and Weapon Systems

The essence of military power is the ability to bring force to bear in order to prevent an enemy from doing something which

---

* *Solid-state physics:* The ability of metals to conduct electricity can be explained in terms of the presence of loosely bound electrons. There is another class of materials in which the electrons, though not so free as those in metals, do nevertheless have a degree of mobility within limits; and there are also materials which have the capability, again within certain limits, of "taking up" electrons. Materials of this kind are called semiconductors and are used in transistors, and the study of their properties is known as "solid-state physics."

† *Servomechanism:* A servomechanism is a device which automatically adjusts some physical characteristic of a system—pressure, voltage, velocity, acceleration, for example—in sympathy with a control signal. It does this through a process of feedback in which any difference between the required output and the actual output is used to bring about further adjustment; this process continues until the difference between the two is zero. Servomechanisms are in common use in the control systems of aircraft and missiles and are to be found also in the power-assisted steering and braking of many modern motor vehicles.

is hostile to one's interests. In practice, force means that one must stop one's adversary, if need be, by killing him; and if that cannot be done in a precise way, it has become military doctrine that everything around him should be destroyed in the effort to stop him. Over the years this has implied an evolution from hand-to-hand fighting to an ability to fire ballistic missiles, armed with nuclear warheads, over thousands of miles, with a relative accuracy greater than that which any expert marksman could ever hope to achieve on a rifle range. Because of the advent of nuclear weapons, hand-to-hand combat has evolved into the possibility of destroying utterly, and with a single blow, enormous cities thousands of miles away.

Over the past twenty-five years there has been an unceasing race between the great powers to increase the range, speed, accuracy and payload of aircraft, and to replace them by missiles as the delivery systems of weapons of destruction. Given the requisite endurance, a few years ago it would have taken the fastest aircraft, say, twenty hours to fly from the midwest of America to Moscow. Today a Minuteman ballistic missile can travel the distance in thirty minutes, and be more certain of finding its target. The technological achievement which the Polaris concept implies is even more astonishing, for here the missile is launched onto its ballistic path not from a fixed point on land, but from any one of an infinity of points under the waters. The navigational equipment of the submarine is so precise that at the moment of launch the computing system involved can have fed into it figures which give the exact starting point of the flight path of the missile. Computers instantaneously do the rest of the calculations, which determine such things as the rate at which the solid-fuel motors of the missile burn, and the varying position of the jets necessary to put and keep the missile on its selected ballistic path. All this came about through vast improvements in liquid- and solid-fuel technology, through an enormous advance in inertial navigation techniques based on what were once simple gyroscopes, through a fantastic elaboration of electronic servomechanism devices, and through highly advanced radio techniques. To most people the most spectacular result of all this applied science has no doubt been manned artificial satellites orbiting the earth. To others an even greater technical achievement was the photography of the back of the moon, and the fact that a rocket (Ranger 9) hit its lunar target with an accuracy of four miles in a flight path of over 240,000 miles—an accuracy which corresponds to 3½ seconds of arc;* and that an even greater accuracy was achieved by the American space experts when they successfully directed a rocket equipped with transmitting photographic apparatus over a flight path of 325 million miles to Mars. Great as have been the advances in aeronautics over the past twenty-five years, including the development of supersonic jet aircraft, of vertical-takeoff aircraft and of variable-geometry aircraft, they hardly compare in their strategic significance with those that have been made in rocket technology. Whether either of them affects campaigns of the kind now going on in Southeast Asia is, of course, another matter.

Aircraft and rockets constitute only one facet of the process whereby force is now brought to bear in the exercise of military power. The massing and speeding of movements of men, and the problem of dealing with intelligence and communications, constitute another set of difficulties whose continual amelioration through technology has transformed the military machine.

Improvements in Medicine, Transport and Communication

Until about a hundred years ago battles were fought at relatively close quarters between small armies which by modern standards were hardly mobile at all, and which were only too often ravaged by disease. For example, the few thousand men of

---

* *Second of arc:* An angle of one-sixtieth of a minute of arc, which is itself one-sixtieth of a degree. Two lines at an angle of one second of arc diverge by about one-twentieth of an inch in every 1,000 feet. The more recent direct hit which the Russians scored on the planet Venus is at least as striking an illustration of ballistic accuracy.

Henry V's army at Agincourt were nearly all suffering from dysentery. Until recently it was often the case that military losses due to disease exceeded those which were due to the enemy. With the coming of the railways in the mid-nineteenth century, mobility was improved, but horse-drawn transport still limited movement from railhead to the front line. By the time of the American Civil War in 1861 and the Franco-Prussian War in 1870, armies of between a quarter and half a million could be deployed; but disease still took a heavy toll. The development of antiseptics and improvements in hygiene enabled armies of well over a million to be deployed in the First World War. Since then motor transport has increased mobility to an enormous extent, and the problem of supplying large armies in the field has been considerably eased. Air transport, parachute forces, commando ships, are all part of the story of increasing mobility. But medical problems still exist and new ones continue to crop up. Infectious hepatitis played havoc with Rommel's forces in the front of Alamein in 1942, and if it were not for the unceasing vigilance of the medical authorities concerned, we can have little doubt that the forces now engaged in Vietnam would find themselves contending with obscure tropical diseases as well as mines, mortar fire and bullets.

Developments in cable communications and then the radio have paralleled the increasing ease with which troops can be moved over great distances. Satellite communications will make it even easier to pass information freely over vast distances. The communication networks whose nodal points were previously manned by human operators are giving way to automatic systems in which the computer plays the vital part. The introduction of the computer has already increased what is called "information processing capacity" by thousands of times. Modern command and control systems are based on the linking by telecommunications of complexes of different sensors, such as the giant radars which form part of BMEWS—the Ballistic Missile Early Warning System—of which Fylingdales is the British component.

The Obsolescence of Weapon Systems

BMEWS is the sensory part of the most evolved version of the kind of air-defense system which we had in the Second World War. Its precursor in the pattern of American defense was a system called SAGE, the broad lines of whose history have now emerged from behind the curtain of secrecy by which it was previously shrouded. Since it reveals particularly clearly the nature of today's technological race in the development of weapon systems, the tale which has been set out by two distinguished American scientists who were directly concerned, Dr. Jerome Wiesner and Dr. Herbert York, is worth recounting.[5]

Until Hiroshima and Nagasaki, the threat which air attack against cities posed was the destruction caused by bombs filled with chemical explosives or incendiary mixtures. In the earlier part of the Second World War an ability to destroy on average 10 percent of the raiding forces was sufficient to blunt a bomber offensive.

In the case of air raids on British cities, the damage caused by the 90 percent which on average survived each attack, while still considerable and horrible, was nonetheless within our capacity to withstand. Today, with the threat of nuclear weapons, it would be beyond any country's capacity to tolerate the penetration of 10 percent of a powerful attacking force, even on a single occasion. In two decades the task of the defense has become, according to Wiesner and York, at least one hundred times more difficult. This is the ratio of an attrition rate of 10 percent, which formerly meant a successful defense, and a penetration ratio of 10 percent, which today would give complete success to the offense. The 10 percent of the attack which would succeed could cause final and utter destruction.

The defensive system SAGE, which the U.S.A. planned early in the 1950s, was designed to prevent enemy bombers from penetrating their territory. The whole North American continent was to be girdled by a system of automatic detectors, whose signals would be fed through a massive system of communications into computers, which would analyze the threat, instantaneously compute the best method of dealing with it and automatically transmit commands to various interceptor systems. These included fighter aircraft, Bomarc (a surface-to-air guided weapon like Britain's Bloodhound), and Nike Hercules, a ballistic rocket. SAGE was designed to have sufficient capacity to deal with the heaviest attack which it seemed possible could be launched against the United States.

The planned date of full operational deployment of this system has come and gone, but nothing like the capability originally planned was ever achieved. The reason for this was that production dates "slipped," subsystems failed to reach the levels of effectiveness which were planned, and costs increased far above estimates (a problem of which we in Britain also have bitter experience).

But these reasons for failure were completely overshadowed by the fact that the kind of offensive against which the system was basically designed changed dramatically when it became clear, in 1958, that the U.S.S.R. had it in her power to attack the U.S.A. not only with bombers but also by missiles. Missiles could "easily" destroy the relatively small number of "soft" but vital parts of the SAGE system, after which bombers, if the U.S.S.R. so decided, could penetrate the American skies unmolested. SAGE, which, if circumstances had not changed, might by now have been fully deployed, and which should have had a highly effective lifetime of about ten years, never came into existence in the form in which it was designed. Thousands of millions of dollars had been spent on it.

To counter the intercontinental ballistic missile, plans were then laid to develop a defense system called NIKE-ZEUS to protect the regions around fifty or so of the biggest American cities. Incoming warheads would be detected by radar, whose signals would be fed direct to computers, which would automatically issue launching and guidance instructions to defensive nuclear missiles, which would intercept the incoming Russian nuclear missile. But the system proved so vast and complicated, as Kenneth W. Gatland[6] has also pointed out in a recent article, that there was no question of it being widely deployed, and the strategists therefore decided that defense should continue to rest on the power of nuclear retaliation.

The defense of even a few special "point targets" of military importance would provide a demonstration that a system like NIKE-ZEUS could work. But the battle of the offensive against the defensive system never slows down. When NIKE-ZEUS was first thought of, the designers gave themselves the problem of destroying simple incoming warheads, one by one, as they were picked up by radar. This task was formidable enough, since the system had to be something like 100 percent effective if it was to provide an adequate defense against thermonuclear weapons. But no sooner had the designers started their work than rumors began circulating about "penetration aids" to the warheads of ballistic missiles, of decoys, and other devices which confuse radar systems, and about the ejection of several objects from one missile. Even without these technical elaborations, there was always the possibility of saturating the defensive system by multiplying the scale of attack.

NIKE-ZEUS has now followed SAGE. But we know from the open press that the search for an antimissile defense system still goes on, and that the Advanced Research Projects Agency of the American Department of Defense is now spending about 400 million dollars a year on projects in which the basic principles of defense against missiles are being examined. Exactly what the Russians are doing in this field only they know; we can be certain that they are not idle. But in theory it would seem that the race will always be an uneven one, with the odds heavily in favor of the attack. It takes far less both in technical knowledge and in resources to elaborate a ballistic missile so that it can outwit a ballistic-missile defensive system, than it ever will to make such a system, however sophisticated, truly effective. This undoubtedly must have been one of the underlying reasons why a group of distinguished American citizens, headed by Dr.

Wiesner, the late President Kennedy's scientific adviser, and Mr.
Roswell Gilpatric, until recently the U.S. Deputy Secretary of
Defense, have recently advocated in a much publicized report[7]
that a three-year moratorium should be agreed to by the U.S.A.
and U.S.S.R. on work on, and deployment of, antiballistic
missiles. A contrary policy, in the view of the committee, could
only add a new dimension to the arms race.

Scientific Advance as a By-product

The immense costs in terms of money, and even more in
terms of scientific and engineering manpower, which are implied
by even the brief outlines of this story relate only to the direct
influence which today's arms race has on the trends of development of some of the most advanced of what are called "the
science-based" industries. In addition, the race has an indirect
effect on the growth of scientific knowledge. The search for
more advanced weapon systems sometimes exposes gaps in basic
scientific knowledge which can be filled only by assuring that
sufficient resources are made available to scientists working in
relevant fields in universities, or in other institutions which
permit men to carry on research according to their own tastes.
One field of work which in recent years has benefited enormously from this indirect interest of the military in science is
oceanography. Advances in our knowledge of the behavior of the
seas are of immense interest to people concerned with submarine warfare, for around the corner is always the fear that an
opponent might learn something new about, say, the trans-
mission of sound waves in water which will transform present
sonar technology, and so make the detection and identification
of submarines both by other submarines and by surface shipping,
and conversely surface shipping by submarines, much easier than
they are today. This is only one example of basic scientific work
whose cultivation has been encouraged by military interests.
There are several others, including many in the medical and
zoological fields. They all help to illustrate the general thesis

which I defined at the outset of this chapter—that the needs of defense are putting a stamp on the pattern of tomorrow's scientific knowledge and on the trends of today's technological developments.

They also indicate something more. Bitter experience has taught the military, as well as civil servants and politicians, that it is dangerous to embark on ambitious schemes for the development of weapon systems, the components of which have themselves not been proved, and which may even be dependent for their working on basic information that has not yet been gained, or on special materials which have not yet been developed. It is for this reason that an enormous proportion of the six to seven billion dollars which the American government spends annually on defense research and development goes into the development of subsystems and components, such as an aero-engine or an airborne radar, or some new inertial-guidance system, before the American authorities commit themselves to spending the even greater sums on the whole weapon systems—the supersonic aircraft or ballistic missiles—of which they might eventually form part.

The Increasing Cost of Military Technology and Development

There are two immediate major consequences of the increasing technical complexity of modern weapons, and in the longer term, two far-reaching repercussions. The first of the immediate consequences is that the cost of the research and development which goes into the making of any major item of modern military equipment can be enormous, and is frequently so great in relation to the likely sum spent on production that the project has to be abandoned before completion. The British TSR-2 aircraft project, which was canceled early in 1965, had already consumed 125 million pounds in research and development[8]—about the same amount as is spent on recurrent expenditure in all British universities in a year. Skybolt, the air-launched nuclear ballistic missile which the American government was developing, had cost 500 million dollars before it was abandoned.[9] Mauler, a U.S. antiaircraft missile, was recently canceled, after 200 million dollars had been spent on its development.[10] Projects such as these are canceled not only because they cost enormous sums in relation to the military needs they are designed to satisfy, but also because it becomes clear as development proceeds that certain technical problems which at the start it had been assumed could be overcome become far too difficult to solve—and the longer it takes to complete a project, the more costly it becomes. In the case of the United Kingdom, we rarely deal with even a successful advanced project whose development costs are less than, say, a half of the total cost of developing and producing the new weapon in numbers sufficient to satisfy our own requirements.

Forty years ago the arms race was still, to a large extent, a race for quantity, even though in some cases radical improvements in quality—e.g., naval fire-control equipment—had great effects on warfare. In the more recent past it has been a race for quality—at whatever point the race was entered. The characteristics of weapon systems which are easiest to achieve have already been achieved by harnessing the technological knowledge which we have available. Each further step is likely to be more demanding and more expensive than the one that went before. (But as I have already suggested, there are indications that the equipment which is most advanced technically will not necessarily prove the most useful in the kind of wars in which the world is now engaged.)

The second immediate consequence of the increasing technical complexity of weapons is that with few exceptions, each new unit, in each new generation, within classes of equipment, produced in the arms race between the greater powers, costs much more per unit weapon than the one it replaces. The increase varies in scale between different types of equipment, but even when one makes full allowances for the effects of inflation, one cannot find any examples, except possibly where standard items are concerned, where the application of more science and technology has led to a reduction in the costs of individual weapons.[11] The cost of naval vessels and other equipment in which the heavy engineering industry is involved about doubles between successive generations. The last generation of British medium bombers were about ten times as expensive as their prewar counterparts. Our present-day fighters are about sixteen times as expensive as the Spitfires and Hurricanes of the Second World War. The cost of new radars today is about ten times that of those produced ten years ago. This is not the end of the story. Each new generation of equipment makes greater demands than its predecessor for skilled supporting personnel. It is true that the aim is generally to put into the hands of the front-line soldiers equipment which is more certain in its operation and which calls for less maintenance at that level. But if this aim is realized, the problem of skilled manpower is not solved; it is merely shifted to another level, and rationally it does not matter whether this level is military or civilian—the trained men have to be found somewhere.

The Inexorable Law

Because of the increasing complexity and cost of weapons, there is a trend which the present British Prime Minister has likened to an "inexorable law"[12] affecting the cost of defense research and development, which in the U.K. now amounts to nearly 15 percent of all money going to defense—an annual levy of about five pounds per man, woman and child in the country. In the United States the figure is more than fifty dollars, if one includes space research. This is the first of the long-term, far-reaching repercussions to which I referred.

If a country wishes its forces to live up to the standards set by the arms race between the superpowers, it must re-equip them at frequent intervals with weapons which are more sophisticated and therefore much more expensive than previous equipment. Considerations of the absolute size of the economy come into play at this point. The cost of developing a weapon system of a given degree of sophistication is much the same in all advanced industrialized countries. But the greater the "buy" over which these costs can be spread, the lower the resultant unit cost. For this reason alone, the United States and the Soviet Union by their very size can, therefore, always expect to produce sophisticated weapon systems more cheaply than we can in Britain.

Let us suppose that as the Gross National Product rises, as a result of the greater productivity of a more or less static working population—the latter being Britain's lot at the moment—defense continues to draw off the same proportion each year. Would we be able, to use the American term, "to buy more defense," because of the greater absolute amount of money that would be going to the armed forces? (I am speaking, of course, in terms of money values standardized to take account of the effects of inflation.) The answer is "No." New aircraft, new surface-to-air missiles, new radars cost more than their predecessors, while improvements in the sophistication or effectiveness of our own weapon systems tend to be canceled out by those of our enemies' weapons. A more expensive offensive system is countered by an even more expensive defense. The net result is an increase in expenditure on defense equipment by both parties—I am talking here about the race between the Western and Soviet blocs—and usually an increase in the security of neither.

But, on the other hand, if one side or the other unilaterally curtailed its defense expenditure, it would soon find itself at a military disadvantage. This is the fear that lies behind the arms race. The pace of this race is not of the U.K.'s determining; it is set for the world by the two superpowers.

We also have to remember that about half of the annual defense vote is consumed by pay, pensions, housing, feeding and clothing. The other half goes to building of one sort or another —for example, barracks and airfields—on the purchase of weapons, including ships and aircraft, and on research and development. As fast as the Gross National Product rises, so there is a corresponding rise in the cost of providing for the men the services need. Only to a small extent do the armed services consume goods whose relative costs are decreasing as a result of increases in productivity in the industries concerned. Assuming that the proportion of the G.N.P. that goes to defense remains constant, this means that, at best, not more than the same proportion of the defense budget would be available each year for procurement and research.

But as everyone knows, the absolute amount available is already not enough, in the case of the U.K., to provide what the forces believe they need.

Each new generation of weapons, as I have already emphasized, costs more than its predecessor. Unless, therefore, we were prepared to spend an increasing proportion of our Gross National Product on defense, we could afford increasingly expensive re-equipment only if we accepted forces of a diminishing size (diminishing, that is, in terms of uniformed manpower, not necessarily of fire power). In fact, as the British government's economic plan has indicated, it is hoped that defense spending over the next five years will be held so that by 1970 it does not exceed 2,000 million pounds at 1964 prices.

The consequences of the costs of increasing sophistication—which we would have had to face sooner or later, whether or not 2,000 million pounds had been set as the ceiling of defense expenditure for 1970—can be abated to a certain extent, but are nonetheless inescapable. The first measure which to some extent mitigates is choosing weapons that are being produced in greater quantity than the ones they replace. This, in practice, would mean a smaller variety of equipment—and since weapons are usually highly specialized for different roles, the result might be having to give up certain military roles. Another measure which could mitigate would be to lessen the load of research and development costs—which, as I have said, are rarely less in the U.K. than one-half of the cost of development and production—by cooperating with other countries. A third and related measure is trying to avoid the research costs—if possible entirely—by buying weapons that are being produced abroad in quantity for several countries.

But not one of these measures is more than a palliative. Even

with larger-scale production, new equipment tends to be much
more expensive than what precedes it. (Indeed, it is so expensive
that without special efforts at standardization it is bound to be
ordered in smaller quantities than before.) The long-term consequences are, therefore, inescapable. If we in the U.K. are to be
efficient in defense, we cannot plan on allowing our equipment
to become obsolete. Equally, we cannot assume that a rising
share of the Gross National Product will bc allotted to defense.
Therefore, the alternatives between which we are forced to
choose are to plan on altering our tasks so as to avoid the need to
introduce some of the most expensive new weapon systems; or
to make our forces smaller; or a combination of both these
measures. The aim of the defense review which the government
has just completed is to see how these things can be done without detriment to Britain's position in the world.

The Diversion of Technological Resources

The second of the more general, as well as long-term, repercussions of the impact of modern technology on defense is that
the scientific resources which are consumed in the process
could, at least in theory, be more usefully employed in the civil
sector of industry. The words "in theory" have to be added to
this proposition since it is impossible to know what our scientific
resources would have been if the needs of defense had not
influenced the direction in which at least part of them grew.[13]
There cannot be the slightest doubt that they have done this. As
I have shown, the needs of defense, or the presumed needs of
defense, to a considerable extent condition the kind of technology, and to a lesser extent the kind of science, that is encouraged in countries which by political circumstances have been
forced into the arms race. Since scientists and engineers are
usually highly specialized, it is by no means certain that the
expertise which has been stimulated by the needs of "defense
industry" can always be fruitfully employed in other sectors of
industry.

In a democracy it is far easier for a government to promote the growth of those industries for whose output it is the sole or main consumer, as is the case with defense industry, than to support technical developments in industries which operate in the open market on a purely commercial basis. It is because a solution must be found to the problem of encouraging civil industry to put modern science to work that the present U.K. government has established a Ministry of Technology. The problem of diverting to civil purposes the scientific resources which now go to defense is again one which any government would have to face if a major goal of national policy, that of arms control through measures of disarmament, were reached, or if the British government could be released from certain of the defense commitments with which it is now saddled, and so of the need to undertake certain special kinds of highly expensive research and development.

But the problem of redeploying the trained scientific and engineering manpower, which in an ideal world could immediately be diverted from defense to civil interests, can sometimes prove difficult.

I referred at the outset of this chapter to the scale of the American commitment to defense industry. With a labor force of only 25 millions, that of the U.K. is also considerable. According to present estimates, the government is now responsible for the employment of 1,400,000 men and women in its own defense establishments and in defense industry. Defense is also responsible for 40 percent of the country's total research and development bill, and uses 20 percent of all scientists and engineers employed in the U.K. on research and development (it accounts for just over half the total resources for science and engineering made available by the government). Given that a relaxation in our defense effort becomes possible, what we have to try to ensure is that our science-based industries—those on which we now depend for the production of our modern weapon systems—can sell goods based on the application of advanced science in any market of the world which allows of fair competition.

"Fallout"

I shall only touch on the question of the secondary benefits which industry derives in civil commercial markets from development contracts for defense equipment—a question which is often referred to as technological "fallout" or "spin-off." Obviously there are some benefits of a general kind, particularly in the electronics and aviation industries. A committee, under the chairmanship of Lord Plowden, which has recently inquired into the British aircraft industry[14] has described the fallout as important, particularly in the fields of digital computers, hydraulic systems, gas turbines and electronics, and has concluded that "no other single industry would have such a pervasive effect on the technological progress of the nation."

This is not a universal view. However much the demands of the military contributed, before the days of the industrial revolution, to the growth of science and to our knowledge of engineering processes, others who have studied the problem hold that defense contracts are now an odd way of deriving technical knowledge which might be useful to modern civil industry. And the Plowden Committee also felt it necessary to qualify its conclusion in the further statement that "greater scientific and technical progress might be achieved if the scientists and technologists now in the aircraft industry worked directly on problems concerning the whole range of British Industry."

John Rubel,[15] who for four years was Assistant Secretary in the American Department of Defense, and Deputy Director of Research and Engineering, has recently pointed out that most of the research and development which is funded by the United States government, and essentially by the Department of Defense, is performed "by industries and concerns that contribute much less to Gross National Product than others that receive little or no research and development funds from the government—and furnish very few of their own." Defense work is, in fact, carried out by only a relatively small percentage of U.S.

business firms, although some of those which are concerned are not only very big undertakings indeed, but also all but totally dependent on defense contracts.[16]

Assuming that one could define what new applied knowledge was wanted in civil industry, the same information could in theory be attained much more cheaply by a direct route than as "spin-off" from research and development into new weapon systems. Examples of a few major canceled defense projects indicate only too clearly how little that is of precise technological value can be gained from vast expenditures on weapon systems.

Most people also believe that "fallout," "spill-over," or "spin-off," whatever one chooses to call the phenomenon, is far more enduring and pervasive in its effects when it derives from the fruits of basic scientific research than when it derives from those of applied science. When Fleming revealed the nature of anti-biotic action, he did far more than discover penicillin; he opened up a vast new field of basic science and of scientific application. So did Faraday when he discovered the interrelation of electricity and magnetism. And even more did Einstein with his simple equation $E = mc^2$. J. J. Thomson's aphorism[17] that "research in applied science leads to reforms; research in pure science to revolutions" may have overstated the case, but its underlying truth is plain to all who have been concerned with the scientific process.

I am back at the question which I touched on in the opening of the first chapter—does war or the threat of war stimulate the growth of science? I do not know what the final answer to this question will prove to be. I myself belief that a state of war can stimulate the scientist to great feats of the imagination and to great practical achievement. Haber's nitrogen-fixation process of the First World War is only one example. The achievement of a nuclear chain reaction in the Second World War is another.

But it is equally true that during the period of the Second World War scientists abandoned, or slowed down, the basic researches they had been carrying out in peacetime, and started exploring, either under their own volition or by direction, other problems which seemed more important to the war effort. In these circumstances, most of them enjoyed resources on a scale they had never dreamed of in peace, in the same way as we hear today of military space laboratories for which more money has already been assigned than would be necessary to maintain the capital and current revenue of all British universities for three years. But I do not know of any of these wartime researches yielding results as far-reaching as those which had been revealed in years of peace.

The belief that the progress of scientific knowledge is accelerated under the stimulus of military need must, therefore, be viewed with suspicion. The fundamental scientific discoveries on which the great technical achievements of the Second World War were based were made well before the war. According to de Solla Price,[18] the postwar size and growth of science, measured in terms of crude size of manpower and published work, is simply an extrapolation of a centuries-old growth rate.

Conclusion

In general, one has to conclude, almost tautologically, that the changing nature of the technology which goes into defense mirrors the changing face of science itself. In the final analysis, the latter is determined by the vision of the individual genius, operating on the body of past scientific knowledge, and in these days, assisted by teams of lesser scientists. As Sir Cyril Hinshelwood[19] said in his Presidential Address to 1965's British Association for the Advancement of Science: "Anybody can state a goal, whether the cure of the common cold or the control of the weather, and the proper organization may provide money for the effort. But inspiration comes only to rare individuals: it floats up intuitively from the subconscious. It is communicable from a leader to a team only if the members have confidence in him, both as a man and as a scientist . . . The famous Fleming mold," he went on to say, "would not have meant much to an administrator, or even a nuclear physicist." It required Fleming's particular genius to realize the significance of his unexpected observation.

And as Polanyi[20] wrote, "a technology must declare itself in favor of a definite set of advantages, and tell people what to do in order to secure them. Technology teaches only actions to be undertaken for *material* advantages by the use of *implements* according to (more or less) *specifiable rules*." The same thought has recently been put more forcefully by Admiral Rickover,[21] one of the most far-seeing and potent technologists of our age: "Technology is tools, techniques, procedures, things; the artifacts fashioned by modern industrial man to increase his powers of mind and body." These implements and procedures do not dictate how they should be used, nor can technology, the directions of whose advance are determined by human decision, claim the authority of science, whose findings, wherever they lead in action, are enduring in the fields of knowledge to which they relate. Those who engage in the debate about the ways modern science should be exploited need, therefore, to comprehend and respect the laws of science applicable to the particular technologies which they wish to exploit.

The exigencies of defense, as well as the demands of urgent decision, have in the past often made it politic to turn a blind eye to these precepts. But the consequences of the focusing of advanced technology on the development of weapons of war begin to reveal themselves more clearly now than they ever have in the past, not only in the military field, but also in wider economic and political spheres. The revelation applies not only to the United Kingdom, but even to the superpowers. Society is beginning to move to a vantage point where it is better able than before to exercise democratic decision about the extent to which technology should transform military affairs; and conversely, where it can better appreciate the extent to which the technologies—as well as science—demanded by defense condition the knowledge, experience and actions of our successors.

3

Facts and Reason in a Nuclear Age

ONE OF OUR MORE COMFORTING HABITS IS AN ABILITY "TO TAKE things as they come," to accept almost unquestioningly the conceptual and material world into which we are born. When the earth was "flat" it remained flat until the effects of Copernicus' teaching gradually made it round. We need not doubt that our "conventional wisdom," to use Kenneth Galbraith's apt phrase,[1] contains other "flat world" myths with which we shall continue to live in peace and happiness until their turn comes to be exploded. On the material side, we grumble about traffic congestion, and rising prices, but there is scarcely a person in our wide world who would not make that congestion worse through the possession of his own motorcar, or who through his own mounting consumer demand would not help to drive prices higher. Whatever it may have been like before the industrial revolution, the man in the street now takes the ideas of science and the fruits of technology for granted, without asking from what seed they spring, how they work, or what may be their social repercussions. Rising standards of living spreading through the world generate a demand for more and more applications of science. Throughout the world, rich and poor alike insist that science, technology and industry should prosper as the panacea against poverty and as the signpost to happiness. Rarely, if ever, has mankind turned its back on any new "thing" that someone has produced through the technological exploitation of scientific knowledge.

We accept electric light and power without knowing how they came about or how they work. We use the telephone and play the phonograph without knowing the scientific principles by which either operates. Radio and television we take for granted. We wear clothes of synthetic textiles, and take aspirin, antibiotics and tranquillizers as and when we want, without knowing either the chemistry of these substances or worrying about possible "side effects." We do so in the assurance that the technological world of today is a firm and sound one, and one which promises to be richer tomorrow. We ask no questions, because with increasing specialization, we know that if our television set breaks down, we have only to call in the television man; or if our motorcar stops running, there is always a garage around the corner; or if we get sick, there is always a doctor.

Only rarely do we find the expert less a person than we thought he was, and only rarely does our confidence in technology break down, or threaten to break down. We have our thalidomide tragedies. We know that people are worried about the repercussions of the use of certain modern pesticides and herbicides—for example, the organophosphorus compounds.* We know that experts are divided in their views about the deleterious effects of the exhaust fumes of motorcars, and about industrial waste gases. We know that there is debate about the wisdom of doctoring animal feeding stuffs with estrogens† in order to improve the efficiency with which cattle convert into flesh the compound cake they are fed. But in all these cases we also know that, given an opportunity to collect more scientific data in a dispassionate way, untrammeled by commercial pres-

---

* *Organophosphorus compounds:* These are organic compounds containing combined phosphorus. The term is normally applied to the highly toxic compounds exemplified by the nerve gases and by modern systemic insecticides (such as tetra-ethyl-pyrophosphate—T.E.P.P.). The important practical characteristic of these materials used as insecticides is that they retain their activity after absorption by plants.

† *Estrogens:* Female sex hormones of essentially ovarian origin which, in conjunction with other hormones, induce the cyclical changes associated with "heat" in the lower mammals and menstruation in apes and humans. The purpose of feeding estrogens to animals is to produce a "fleshier" beast.

sures, the experts will in all likelihood agree about the potential hazards of whatever application of science is in doubt; or, if they do not all agree, that a clear majority opinion will emerge.

The Abstractions of Nuclear Weaponry

As I see it, there is one area of technological advance where little of this applies, and that is the field of nuclear weapons. The scientist and applied scientist know about the principles and processes of controlled and uncontrolled nuclear fission and nuclear fusion. They know how to make a wide variety of "ordinary atomic weapons," with yields in the so-called low kiloton range, as well as of hydrogen bombs with yields varying from less than the equivalent of, say, half a million tons of TNT to well-nigh a hundred million tons. From field trials and by extrapolation of the results of laboratory investigation, they know what these weapons would do to buildings and people; about the nature of radioactive contamination; about the effects of the "fire ball" of an atomic explosion; and about the dangers of blast.

But what they do not know is what true meaning should be read into the "concept" of nuclear warfare. Happily for mankind, only two nuclear weapons have so far been exploded in anger, the one that destroyed Hiroshima and the one that flattened Nagasaki. Both had a yield of between 15 and 20 kilotons, and both were used so close to the time when Japan was going to sue for peace anyhow, that there are those who contend that neither weapon accelerated the end of the Pacific war.

In a single flash these two bombs all but effaced two fairly large towns. But that is all we really do know for certain. We do not know if and how such weapons could be used for direct military purposes on the battlefield. We do not know what military value to attach to nuclear landmines and to a host of other nuclear devices. The reason why we do not know is that no country could afford to undertake the "experiments" which would provide any direct information on the subject.

Yet in spite of our ignorance, or in this case because of it, nuclear weapons constitute one of the dominant facts of our lives. Their existence cannot be brushed aside, nor, like any genie, can they be forced back into the bottle from which they were liberated. Nuclear power constitutes one of the dominant features of the international landscape, one of the basic facts with which all politicians must reckon—like, for example, the accelerating and differential pace with which world population is growing.

If there is to be informed and rational talk about the use of nuclear weapons, and if there is to be any clear understanding of the policies which the British government has been trying to realize and pursue, it is necessary to put flesh on some of the abstractions which have grown up in discussions of nuclear weapons, on measures such as "kiloton" and "megaton," on terms such as "tactical" and "strategic" nuclear weapons, on words like "deterrence," "escalation" and "doomsday machines." Fortunately, there is a mass of published data on which to call in order to do this. Indeed, there is probably nothing in the secret archives of the nuclear powers which can help one to appreciate the issues at stake any better than what has already been published under official auspices.[2]

A Megaton on a City

There is no need here to outline the physical processes of nuclear fission and nuclear fusion, and their roles in nuclear weapons, whether of the kiloton or megaton categories. To start I shall instead try to provide a description of the effects of a single ground burst of a one-megaton weapon dropped on a large city, and a 20-kiloton weapon exploded in the middle of, say, a medium-size town. It is necessary to do this if we are to reach any comprehension at all of what an attack by nuclear weapons would mean. The scale of instantaneous destruction which such weapons would cause is so much greater than anything that has ever been seen by man that we must pin ourselves to familiar examples in order to avoid slipping into meaningless generalities. For example, it is totally beyond my capacity to understand what some writers on nuclear strategy think they are saying when they talk about a "nuclear exchange" in which the United States alone would suffer something like 100 million fatal casualties in a single strike, and when they then go on to imply, by the use of words unrelated to any experience, that the survivors could reconstitute a great and thriving civilization. Whether or not it is conceivable that in any circumstances, accidental or deliberate, a single large city would ever be attacked in isolation by a megaton weapon, we must start with simpler pictures if we are not to go on generating meaningless unrealities about nuclear war.

From nuclear tests that have been carried out in the atmosphere, we know the distances from a burst to which zones of radioactive contamination would spread and with what declining intensity; we know the area of risk from instantaneous fire; and we know how the pressure of the shock or blast wave falls as it moves from the center of the burst at a speed faster than that of sound. In order to understand what this might add up to in real life, we have to apply this technical information to the makeup of a particular city, or of a series of particular cities—for no two of them are the same. Cities and towns vary in layout and in their overall density of population; the density of housing varies in different parts of the city; some areas are devoted to industry and commerce and others to housing; the water supply of one town comes in, and is distributed, differently from that of another; power stations are not distributed in a uniform fashion; sewage systems differ in their layout; food markets are variously distributed, as are also the bakeries. In short, there is no uniform pattern to a city, nor do we find that within a city one district exactly reproduces another. One also has to remember that if a city were attacked by a nuclear weapon, or weapons, the results would vary according to the position of the burst, or bursts, in relation to both the geography of the city and the time of the attack.

Because of these variations, the only way to achieve a realistic picture of the effects of a nuclear weapon in a populated area is to focus on a city or town one knows, and to build up the story from the sum of the likely facts as they would occur in the smallest units that are defined for normal administrative purposes. Only in that way can one start to derive a "human picture" of what would happen.

Let us imagine a large British city, say, Birmingham, with a population of about one million and where a one-megaton bomb, just a single bomb, exploded close to ground level about a mile or so from its center. A detailed analysis would very likely show that a third of its inhabitants would be immediately killed as a result of blast and fire, or die from a lethal dose of radiation in the first two days. Most would be killed by the blast wave which would tear their houses apart, and in the debris of which survivors would remain trapped. In addition, about another hundred thousand would be serious casualties unable to look after themselves. That means that only about half of our original population would be alive and able to cope with the situation by which they would be confronted immediately after the explosion—although numbers of them might later become casualties from radiation.

But what would the situation be? Within a radius of about a couple of miles from the point of burst of the bomb, there would be total destruction and practically no survivors at all. Farther away the incidence of casualties would fall and their severity would decline. Hardly a house anywhere would not have been damaged to a greater or lesser extent. The likelihood is that only about a third could still be lived in, although roofs, doors and windows would have been damaged everywhere. Depending on the direction of the prevailing wind, the whole built-up area to one or other side of the point of burst would have been affected by radioactive fallout. Fires would be raging and spreading everywhere.

Essential services would have ceased to exist in the main area of destruction. What remained elsewhere would depend entirely upon the way the services had been laid out. Parts of the city which might not have been affected by the direct effects of the blast, or even by radioactive fallout, could find themselves without water or drainage, power supplies or bakeries.

In short, the explosion of a single megaton weapon over one of our large cities would almost incvitably lead to its total elimination. Those who had been trapped in the wreckage of buildings and who could still fend for themselves would know that if they themselves could not crawl to safety, the chances would be that there would be no one to help them. Able survivors would be either fleeing or searching for food, for relations, for help, or for some place of shelter better than the one in which they happened to be when the bomb went off.

If one could concentrate into one focal point and one focal moment all the destruction which Britain suffered in the Second World War, the picture would not be as bad as the one that needs to be conjured up when one talks of the explosion of a single megaton weapon. However improbable it may be that such a weapon would ever be used, one also has to remember that were this to happen, it would not be one city which would run the risk of attack, but several, and not one megaton on a target, but several.

If Birmingham were a target, the chances are that Coventry, Bristol, Manchester, Liverpool, not to speak of London, would also be targets. We have to compound the picture of disaster I have painted. Since there are few cities with a population of more than a million, we also have to remember that a megaton burst over a smaller city, with a population of, say, a quarter of a million, would cause relatively more intense destruction.

Kilotons and Multimegatons

Let us turn to the lower end of the scale, and imagine that a 20-kiloton bomb, that is to say, a bomb with a fiftieth the power of a megaton, burst in the center of a smaller town, a town like Carlisle, with a population of 70,000 people, and with some 25,000 buildings. Roughly speaking, the scale of destruction would be relatively the same as for the megaton weapon which burst over the city with a population of a million. Thousands of houses would be immediately destroyed, and others would be in flames. Once more one would not expect to find a single house untouched. The proportion of people killed or wounded might be the same or a little less than what one would expect on a pro rata basis with the megaton burst over our model one-million city, but the survivors would have just as terrifying a problem to contend with as would occur in any larger city—fires, roads blocked, no water supply, no sources of food, radioactive fallout and so on.

A point that needs to be made is that the radius of destruction from the burst of a nuclear weapon does not vary directly with the energy yield, but is proportional to the cube root of the yield. If, for example, the radius of total destruction was three miles with a 4-megaton weapon, it would require only one of about 1¼ megatons to have a corresponding effect over a radius of two miles, and a 160-kiloton (= 0.16 megaton) bomb to do as much damage over an area with a radius of one mile. By present-day standards a 20-kiloton bomb is referred to as a small weapon. Smaller ones are, of course, also made, but even if only a one-kiloton nuclear weapon were used in an inhabited area, the immediate destruction and number of casualties would be far greater than anything which was ever experienced in any single incident during the Second World War, not to mention the additional and more enduring hazard introduced by radioactive fallout.

At the higher end of the scale, there are, of course, the multi-megaton weapons. In one of their series of tests over their Arctic testing grounds, the U.S.S.R. exploded a weapon which had a yield of about 60 megatons. Its effects were such that Mr. Khrushchev is reported to have said that the Russians had decided not to explode a bigger bomb for fear that all the windows of Moscow, hundreds of miles away, would have been broken! Following this explosion, some experienced nuclear physicists let it be known that weapons with a yield of 100 megatons or more could be exploded outside the atmosphere over a country and, for reasons into which I need not enter, destroy hundreds of square miles of that country utterly by means of a single heat flash. Other calculations which have been published suggest that multimegaton weapons could be exploded in ships near coastlines, so creating enormous tidal waves which would engulf everything within miles of the shore.

Let me now turn from the abstractions kilo, mega and multi-mega to the concepts of "strategic" and "tactical" weapons and wars.

Tactical and Strategic Nuclear Weapons

The terms "tactics" and "strategy" have become considerably transformed over the years. The Oxford Dictionary defines "tactics" as "the art or science of deploying military or naval forces in order of battle, and of performing warlike evolutions and maneuvers." "Strategy" constitutes "the art of projecting and directing the larger military movements and operations of a campaign." In essence, the concept of "strategy" thus relates to decisions about forces not yet committed to actual fighting, while "tactics" relates to the manner and control of forces in contact with an enemy. The boundary between the two terms has obviously always been indistinct and variable, since what may be a matter of tactics at one level of decision often becomes a strategic consideration at another. To take an extreme example, some Supreme Commander fighting a major war in, let us say, Europe might regard it as a tactical consideration to abandon temporarily a small country to the enemy. Such a decision would, however, obviously be a matter of the highest strategic significance to the government of the country concerned.

The two terms have also become strangely confused in the classification of weapons, and particularly where air power is concerned. At the end of the First World War Lord Trenchard, the first of the great British air commanders, and the Italian General Douhet[3] began to urge the view that the best way to use an air force in the attainment of victory was to bomb the enemy's homeland. This concept became the basis of the organization not only of the British, but of all countries' air forces into bomber and fighter commands. It was also the basis of the strategic air war which the British, the Americans and the Germans waged during the Second World War. During that war, however, we also employed our air forces to assist in land battles by striking at targets within the battle zone. The aircraft set aside for this task became known as tactical aircraft, even if they were often the same as those which had been used in so-called strategic attacks.

Since that time the radius of action over which so-called "tactical aircraft" are conceived as operating in support of land forces is as great as that over which our strategic bombers operated in the Second World War.

The confusion becomes even greater when the terms "strategic" and "tactical" are related to actual weapons. For example, people talk today of megaton weapons mainly as strategic weapons, while most military planners in the West talk of 20- or 10-kiloton weapons as tactical weapons—regardless of the enormous destruction these weapons would cause if used in any area of battle in any well-populated country.

The Concept of Strategic Nuclear Deterrence

How does all this relate to the concept of strategic deterrence, about which so much has been written that all one needs do is try to simplify?

The devastation of Hiroshima and then of Nagasaki in 1945 revealed to the world that the United States and Britain could make weapons of destruction thousands of times more fearful than any that had ever been known before. Then three years before the U.K. exploded its own first atomic weapon, we learned that the secret of the bomb was known also to the Russians. That was in 1949, just about the time when conditions in Europe, and particularly the extension of the area of Russian domination, had led to the formation of the North Atlantic Treaty Organization—N.A.T.O.—as a defensive alliance whose purpose was to prevent the U.S.S.R. from extending still farther the area over which it held political sway.

For a time, however, the West believed that it held the advantage in nuclear weapons, and that its bomber forces were far more powerful than the Russian. So in 1954, John Foster Dulles,[4] then the American Secretary of State, declared the doctrine of "massive retaliation," that is, that the U.S. would "depend primarily upon a great capacity to retaliate instantly by means and at places of its own choosing" to deter aggression. Almost simultaneously the grim threat of mutual retaliation on each other's homelands, by means of long-range aircraft, started taking shape.

Next came a quantum-like transformation of the scene. The Russians demonstrated that they could deliver nuclear warheads not only by aircraft, but also by means of intercontinental ballistic missiles. This gave a new twist to the arms race, as the United States accelerated its work in the same field of armaments. Slowly the realization grew that were the West, and in particular the United States, to use nuclear weapons against the Russian homeland, the Russians would undoubtedly retaliate in kind, however much smaller their nuclear armory might be in numerical terms. The concept of mutual strategic deterrence had started to evolve, and with it the belief that since neither side knew whether the other would be the first to unleash a nuclear war, it was essential that both developed the means whereby they could retaliate, whatever the damage they had suffered from what became known as "a first strike" from the other side. A retaliatory nuclear force had to be invulnerable, a term probably first used in this connection by the late Sir Winston Churchill,[5] and various techniques were evolved in order to achieve this end.

Today the invulnerability of "deterrent nuclear forces" has been achieved in two main ways, both based upon the deployment of intercontinental nuclear ballistic missiles. One method has been to disperse these weapons, for example the American Minuteman, over wide areas in highly protected silos underground; or as the Russians claim they have done, on mobile launchers which no "satellite eye" can detect. The second is the Polaris submarine technique, where the missiles are deployed in virtually undetectable mobile platforms under the seas. Whichever way they are deployed, the weapons are pretargeted on vital objectives in the country of the potential enemy.

In this way a condition of mutual strategic deterrence has been established between the Western and Soviet blocs; and so far neither side has risked any action which might trigger an all-out exchange—although the Cuban "incident" showed that what seemed like "nuclear brinkmanship" could be carried to a very dangerous extreme.[6]

Many American writers, of whom Herman Kahn and Thomas Schelling[7] are among the more celebrated, have theorized on this situation, and have tried to argue that in the rational world in which we live, the Eastern and Western blocs, if they were at war, could move by gradual and measured steps of nuclear escalation to a position in which they would virtually have destroyed all their major centers of population, as well as all their so-called military targets. The same writers have tried to pretend that were such a state of affairs to come about, and hundreds of millions of people to be killed both in the Western world and in the U.S.S.R., it could still be possible for the few remaining survivors to reconstruct a new world on the radioactive debris of the old. This kind of writing has been widely accepted as a new form of scientific analysis and as the textbooks of the nuclear age. It certainly takes into account the facts about nuclear explosions as given in official statements, as well as information about the accuracy of bombing and of missile attacks. Sometimes it is also dressed in mathematical terms. But I myself find that this particular form of the new strategic literature has little foundation in experience and, in particular, experience of warfare. Moreover, it is based upon assumptions about human behavior which seem totally unreal. It constitutes neither scientific analysis nor scientific theorizing, but is a non-science of untestable speculations about Western- and Soviet-bloc behavior which takes little or no account of the major political changes that are now taking place in China, Africa and other vast areas of the world, and of their effects on the politics of the Western- and Soviet-bloc powers. Whatever else, it is a kind of writing which fails to reflect a realistic appreciation of how people would react and behave if only a single megaton warhead were to explode on only one major center of population.[8] Talk of "nuclear doomsday machines" is even more unrealistic than the rest.

The plain fact is that neither the Western nor the Soviet blocs could ever afford to put the concept of strategic nuclear war to experimental test. The smallest "experiment" might cost millions of lives. Far from an all-out nuclear exchange being a rational action which could ever be justified by any set of conceivable political gains, it is highly unlikely that any country would, in the pursuit of its political objectives, deliberately risk the total destruction of its own capital city, leave alone the destruction of all its major centers of population; or risk the resultant chaos which would leave in doubt a government's ability to remain in control of its people.

But even if the validity of the principle of strategic deterrence, upheld by the threat of retaliation with nuclear weapons, cannot in practice be tested, the political history of the past ten years suggests that the concept is, nonetheless, a real one. The stability of the nuclear balance would thus be dangerously threatened if either side were to devise an effective antiballistic-missile defense capable of intercepting incoming nuclear warheads. My own view on this matter, as I have already indicated, is that the technical problems of this aspect of the arms race are such that the advantage will always remain with the attacker since, at the very least, he could saturate any defensive system and by so doing wreak immeasurable damage—whatever the defenses his missiles would have to penetrate. As I have also indicated, there remains the technical possibility, which has been ventilated in public discussion, of multimegaton nuclear weapons being detonated outside the atmosphere in a way which would most probably preclude the operation of an effective antiballistic-missile defense system. I do not see the main balance of strategic nuclear power being significantly upset in any near future, whatever minor perturbations may occur.

When one dismisses the mumbo-jumbo of the theorists, or some of the abstractions that have grown up in discussions of nuclear weapons, the basic strategic facts of our nuclear age are thus quite simple. First, nuclear weapons exist and cannot be brushed aside. They are at present deployed in thousands by both the United States and the U.S.S.R., and to a much smaller extent by the United Kingdom. France is on the way to becoming an operational nuclear power, while China is in the earlier stages of this process.

Second, the two superpowers, the U.S.A. and the U.S.S.R., who have now been deploying these weapons for several years, have shown by their actions that while they recognize the extreme danger which these weapons imply, to themselves as well as to their enemies, neither is prepared to take any step which might give the other a potential advantage in the nuclear field, so long as there is no settlement to the political differences which separate the Western from the Eastern bloc of nations. Because of the fear that the balance of strategic deterrence might be disrupted, with the advantage dramatically moving to one or the other side, both spend vast sums in trying to solve the considerable technical problems which a defense against ballistic missiles entails. Correspondingly—as has been commonly argued by people who ought to know the facts[9]—there is little reason to suppose that either of the two superpowers could significantly improve its military power by any further elaboration of its nuclear arsenal.

Nuclear Weapons on the Battlefield

I turn now to what has become widely regarded as a sphere of warfare in which nuclear weapons could be used for tactical purposes, i.e., within the battle area itself. In some ways the development of this notion has been as crucial to the history of the world over the past ten years as was the decision to develop the H-bomb. But it happened almost unnoticed. In the United States the former decision was so highly dramatized by the conflict of opinion of two distinguished physicists—Dr. Robert Oppenheimer on the one hand, the man who directed the development of the first nuclear weapon, and Dr. Edward Teller, "the father of the H-bomb," on the other—that it tended to overshadow all other aspects of the recent history of nuclear weapons.[10]

About the time Foster Dulles enunciated his now discredited diplomatic slogan of "massive retaliation," the then N.A.T.O. Council agreed that if war were to break out on European soil between the N.A.T.O. Alliance and the U.S.S.R., any disparity in numbers of men—in those days it was believed that the Russians enjoyed an overwhelming advantage in this respect— would be redressed by the use of nuclear weapons in the battle area. The notion that these weapons could be used as artillery to compensate for inferior numbers of men evolved not as a result of analysis, but mainly as what seemed to be the only hope in a period when the West believed it had at its disposal a far bigger nuclear arsenal than did the U.S.S.R. In the background were the scientists in the weapons laboratories who had been able to show that weapons in the low-kiloton range could be both developed and produced in relatively vast numbers. In the period when H-bombs with the explosive power of millions of tons of TNT enjoyed the limelight, a 10-kiloton bomb, or a one-kiloton bomb, seemed pretty "small beer" as a weapon of destruction!

I have always been, and still remain, skeptical of the notion of tactical nuclear war. In an article[11] which I published in 1961, with the authority of General Lauris Norstad, then Supreme Commander of Land Forces of Europe, and of Admiral of the Fleet Lord Mountbatten, then Chief of the British Defense Staff, I pointed out that the battlefield use of any one of the weapons then in the Western nuclear armory—and presumably also in that of the Russians—would mean the instantaneous and total destruction or elimination of an area varying in size between, say, a large village and a large town. Depending on the way forces were disposed, the explosion of a nuclear weapon of, say, 100 kilotons could mean the elimination of one or of dozens of battle groups, or of one or of several squadrons of aircraft on the ground. But, as I also pointed out, if one's target information happened to be wrong, it could mean the elimination of none.

I went on to argue that an actual nuclear land battle could hardly lead to anything but total chaos, and illustrated the point by reference to a study which had recently taken place and which involved three N.A.T.O. corps. In this operation nuclear weapons were supposed to have been "used" against military targets only, in a 10,000-square-mile area, in which no large towns or cities were "priority targets." In this "battle," which lasted only a few days, it was assumed that the two sides together—although in unequal numbers—used a total of between 20 and 25 megatons in not fewer than 500 and not more than 1,000 strikes. This "study" showed that 3½ million people would have had their homes destroyed if the weapons had been air burst, and 1½ million if ground burst. In the former case, at least half the people concerned would have been fatally or seriously injured. In the case of ground-burst weapons, all 1½ million would have been exposed to a lethal radiological hazard and a further 5 million to serious danger from radiation.

So far as so-called military results were concerned, the "battle" was inconclusive. Today, when both sides have nuclear weapons which they could use on, and in relation to, a battlefield, it is difficult to imagine, at any rate in theory, that it could be otherwise.

One of the obvious tactical consequences of the fact that nuclear weapons might be used in field warfare is that forces would have to be dispersed, since no commander could dare risk concentrating his troops in such a way that large numbers were within the zone of effect of a single nuclear burst. A primary aim of tactics would thus be to dispose minor units* in such a way that no more than one unit would, on average, be vulnerable to a nuclear strike. In addition, forces would have to be made increasingly mobile, while the presumed nuclear battlefield would demand far better apparatus for reconnaissance and surveillance, and for communications, than were ever available in the Second World War.

Problems of judgment and control become increasingly difficult the more one's weapons automatically lead to overhitting—even of strictly military targets. In the ideal, the best weapon is the one just big enough to destroy the specific target against which it is directed. This is true whether looked upon from the standpoint of military practicality or plain economics. For example, both theoretical and field studies of the Second World War battles showed that the smaller the units into which a given weight of antipersonnel weapons was divided, the greater the number of casualties they caused.

In theory, a defending side would have to be ready to fire as many nuclear weapons as would be necessary to reduce the attacking forces to the number of minor units that could be held. If one assumes that an attacking force began with a numerical superiority better than three to one, and that the defenders had no chance of success unless they could reduce their opponent's advantage to about two to one, one can then calculate that hundreds of nuclear weapons might be needed—in theory—by each defending corps. These numbers, fired on a corps front, would cause such physical damage (regardless of the numbers of actual military casualties) as to render the whole

---

* *Minor unit:* A term used particularly in the discussion of land battles to describe a company of infantry, a squadron of tanks, a battery of artillery, or some combination of these of roughly equivalent size—in all, a unit of around a hundred men and their equipment.

idea of mobile or any other form of warfare meaningless. The damage—so far as the battlefield area is concerned—would be as great as one associates with customary estimates of an exchange of strategic nuclear weapons.

These earlier theoretical conclusions have since been borne out by the results of more sophisticated war games.

To obtain a more realistic impression of the circumstances which would actually prevail in such a "limited" nuclear battle, we also need to bear in mind that no such operation, however confined, would be likely to occur without collateral, so-called interdiction, attacks with nuclear weapons well beyond the area of local engagements, the targets being communication centers, distant airfields, missile sites and so on. Clearly, it would require the utmost judgment and control if the nonmilitary effects of nuclear weapons—even if they were directed against presumed military targets—were not to dominate the situation once they had been used. Once they had done so, a new situation would be generated which would be outside all possible military control— as it certainly now is outside all military experience.

In stating this view in my earlier article I was not presuming to suggest that the problem of trying to operate rationally within an environment of chaos was new to military experience and command, or that civilian populations had not suffered from military operations in the past. What I was trying to bring out is that the potential of destruction in nuclear war has assumed such proportions that it moves warfare into a dimension completely different from the one in which we have all gained our experience. Indeed, it would be impossible to say where tactical nuclear war differs from strategic nuclear war, in the same way as one could do no more than hope that the first would not move immediately into the second.

Nothing that has happened in the four years since I published this piece makes it necessary for me to modify the views I then expressed. Indeed, I would hazard the guess that today many more military authorities would share these ideas than were ready to do so four, five years ago. Mr. McNamara's much

publicized "full options"* approach to N.A.T.O. strategy is a far
cry from the belief that any land operation in N.A.T.O. Europe
would immediately "go nuclear." And only recently we have
read that the Russian High Command—which hitherto is supposed to have adhered to the doctrine that any future war would
entail, in the words of Mr. Khrushchev, "the use of nuclear
weapons not only in the first days, but in the first minutes of
war"—now accepts the contrary proposition that there could be
operations in Western Europe in which, following on an attack
by Western forces on Soviet-bloc territory, the fight would be
waged in a nonnuclear or conventional fashion.

My own view is that nuclear weapons deployed in direct
support of forces in the field can only be seen as weapons which
are there to deter aggression. They are not tactical wapons for
use like machine or field guns, but one band in the spectrum of
all deterrent nuclear weapons. The consequences of their being
used are so fearful that a primary purpose of all the nuclear
powers has become that of seeing that the weapons are never
used, at the same time as the message is kept plain that they
would be, given the political decision.[12]

The Dissemination and Control of Nuclear Weapons

The evolution of a simple state of nuclear balance between
the Western and Soviet blocs is, of course, now threatened by
the emergence of France and China as nuclear powers, and by
the fear that other countries might follow in their train. The
belief that the possession of a nuclear arsenal, and of the means
of delivering nuclear weapons accurately over thousands of
miles, is a main reason for the dominance of the superpowers

---

* *Full options policy:* There are, in essence, two approaches to the problem of
deterring a potential enemy from aggression. In the one, the enemy is threatened
at once with unacceptable and inescapable punishment. In the other—the full
options policy—the aim is to demonstrate clearly that the forces available for
defense are sufficient always to ensure that the aggression will not succeed in its
objective. This policy implies that at whatever level the enemy chooses to attack,
he will find an impenetrable defense; and that whatever form his attack may take,
the proper form of defense will be available to frustrate him.

makes a nuclear armory an almost irresistible ambition for many nonnuclear countries who either aspire to power, or suppose that possession of nuclear weapons provides greater military security. A difficulty in persuading nonnuclear countries against this view is that nonnuclear countries anxious to join the "nuclear club" are, in general, far worse informed about the possible nature of nuclear warfare than those who already belong. Similarly, no country which has not yet entered the nuclear race can appreciate the relatively fabulous cost of providing a viable nuclear armory. The nuclear warhead is only the beginning of the story. For these and other reasons, and in particular because of the fear that the multiplication of nuclear powers would make the world even less secure than it is today, a major goal of the United Kingdom's policy has become the achievement of some form of international agreement which will help prevent the further dissemination of nuclear weapons.

This is no new policy. British interest in what was called the "control of the atom" was reflected in the 1946 discussions by the United Nations of the Baruch Plan. But the atom has proved very difficult to control. It was not until three years ago that with two exceptions—France and China—the nations of the world agreed to stop, or if they had not started, not to undertake atmospheric tests of nuclear devices. This occurred when the partial Test Ban Agreement was negotiated in Moscow in July, 1963. It is necessary to consider what factors now prevent the realization of yet a further step toward reason in the nuclear age in which we live—a step which all countries would no doubt like to see taken, but in which interests vary greatly, and consequently frequently cancel each other out.

One of the major considerations which led to the partial Test Ban Treaty was the fact that between July, 1945, when the first experimental atomic bomb was detonated in New Mexico, until the signing of the Test Ban in 1963, contamination of the atmosphere by the radioactive products of nuclear fission, and by the secondary products of radiation, had approached a level which was nearly 10 percent of natural background radiation.

Not unnaturally this caused alarm both in political circles and amongst biologists and medical people who knew what this meant from the point of view of health and heredity. The raising of the level of radiation in our environment was due to the fact, as Wiesner and York[13] have pointed out, that the accumulated tonnage of nuclear explosions had been doubling every three years since 1945. And as they also showed, a chart which plotted the accumulation of radioactive products could be also read as a chart of the acceleration of the arms race between the great powers. Since the Test Ban Treaty, the curve of additional radiation has started to flatten out, a fact which more than justifies the view stated by President Kennedy at the time that the partial Test Ban was an "important first step—a step towards peace, a step towards reason, a step away from war." This sentiment was powerfully echoed in the United Kingdom by the government of the day, and by the leaders of the opposition, now the government in power.

Those who advocated and worked for the partial Test Ban have neither stopped urging that further steps toward reason be taken, nor have they been naïve or unsophisticated about the political issues which are involved. On the political front we are dealing with national priorities, or assumed priorities, which unfortunately vary from country to country. The British government has indicated that it rates a relaxation of East-West tension and a stop to the dissemination of nuclear weapons as more important than all other issues within the political frame where these matters belong. But the nuances which surround these issues do not appear the same to us as they do to some of our allies, let alone some of our enemies. What constitutes "dissemination" is itself a bone of major contention.

Mr. William C. Foster,[14] Head of the Disarmament Agency in the State Department of the United States, has recently published an analysis of the problem in which recommendations are made which do not differ greatly from British official views on the subject. As Mr. Foster points out in his article, significant changes have been occurring over the past few years in Soviet-

American relations which substantially affect the prospects for arms control and disarmament. In particular, the U.S.S.R. is now showing an increased interest in small steps of military relaxation which, while lacking some of the popular appeal of complete and general disarmament, are more likely to be realized in the foreseeable future. Among the steps which have been taken since the signing of the Test Ban Agreement in 1963 are the U.N. resolution banning the arming of artificial satellites with weapons of mass destruction; and the simultaneous announcement by the U.S.A., the U.K. and the U.S.S.R. of "cutbacks" in their planned production of weapons-grade plutonium and uranium. In particular, the U.S.A. and the U.S.S.R., like the United Kingdom have become increasingly concerned about the likelihood that many nations which do not now produce nuclear weapons may find themselves drifting along the nuclear road, at least partly because it will not be long before they have a significant potential to produce plutonium in civil nuclear-power plants of the kind that are now being built in India and Japan. And both the U.S.A. and the U.S.S.R., as well as the U.K., are worried that the expense of developing a nuclear technology, and the associated delivery systems, will exacerbate the economic, and hence the political, problems of the countries concerned. Furthermore, the U.S.S.R., no less than the U.S.A. and the U.K. has become greatly concerned by the fact that China's demonstrated ability to make atom bombs has had a very unsettling effect upon the politics of all Asiatic countries, and particularly in India. There is good reason to agree with Mr. Foster that on these major issues the interests of the U.S.S.R. coincide with our own.

The basic problem in the existing situation seems to be the ambivalent attitude of nonnuclear countries to nuclear weapons, due partly to the conflict between the view that nuclear weapons and delivery systems are on the one hand both immoral and very expensive in resources, and on the other, not only valuable as weapons of war but also the means whereby the greater powers have achieved the dominant position they enjoy in the world.

Some of the nonnuclear countries also fear that the U.S.A., the U.S.S.R. and the U.K. might get together to establish some kind of hegemony, through the threat of using nuclear weapons, over the political and military future of the "have-not" countries.

A large part of this conflict is undoubtedly due to an ignorance of the nature of nuclear weapons as weapons for actual use, as opposed to weapons of deterrence. The public pressure to go nuclear, exerted in countries like India by nontechnical people, is mainly uninformed pressure. But what else is one to expect when the great powers proclaim that they are deploying hundreds or thousands of tactical nuclear weapons with their field armies? How are countries less informed to be made to understand that such devices are there to deter offensive action, and not as weapons to be used like artillery? The message that is conveyed by the facts that nuclear weapons were not used in Korea, or that they are not now being used in Vietnam, or that, in spite of the Foster Dulles doctrine of massive retaliation, they were not used either in the battles which saw the end of French Indochina, or that they were not used to prevent the Russians from suppressing the revolt in Hungary, cannot prevail against the advertised possession of tactical nuclear weapons by the greater powers. Equally striking, but moving in an opposite direction, is the widespread belief that it was the threat of nuclear war which more than anything else determined Russia's withdrawal from the situation she had created when she started installing intermediate-range ballistic missiles (I.R.B.M.'s) in Cuba.

On the whole, it is not surprising at all that to some of the poorer countries which do not possess them, nuclear weapons seem to be the most potent weapons of war and the most powerful defense against aggression. This is the world's danger. The fact that the sophisticated great powers who already possess nuclear weapons have not used them in these hot wars into which they have been drawn over the past fifteen years is no guarantee that they would not be used by less informed and less sophisticated countries. Once nuclear weapons were used, the battle, as well as the effects, could well spread over the entire world, and involve even the greater powers in a nuclear holocaust. It would be cynical to agree with the view that in comparison with the United States and the Soviet Union, some countries may have "relatively little to lose if nuclear weapons are used." But one can well agree with Mr. Foster that "having five nations with nuclear weapons is bad enough and that, if the number is to be limited, the prospects are almost certainly better at five than at six or any higher number."

Mr. Foster is a very highly placed U.S. official now in office. He echoes sentiments which, if not formal U.S. policy, are strongly shared both in the U.K. and in the U.S.S.R. This is the remarkable change in the climate of opinion that has occurred in recent months. The problem of translating these sentiments into action is one of the most acute and urgent which the world has ever had to face. Clearly there is no one solution, since the problem itself appears differently to different countries and different factions. But while time is not on the world's side, and while the issue of dissemination may, in the words of some, soon pass the "point of no return," there is also greater hope now than ever before, simply because of the community of interests in this field between the great nuclear powers. Now that the nuclear strength which they have so painfully built up over the past twenty years has proved not to be synonymous with national security, the problem for them is to achieve a common sense of priorities in the field of disarmament. This is the critical issue before us. Mr. Foster has given his own view that in order to achieve a pact on nondissemination, the U.S. and the U.S.S.R. "would be well advised to stop the strategic nuclear-arms race and destroy some strategic capabilities on a reciprocal basis." He has also in effect asked whether the achievement of world agreement on the problem of dissemination would not be worth while even if it meant some "erosion of alliances resulting from the high degree of U.S.—Soviet cooperation which will be required if a nonproliferation program is to be successful." This is indeed reason in a nuclear age. On the other side is a list of possible compensations for an agreement by the nonnuclear countries not to acquire nuclear weapons—joint guarantees against aggression, economic aid, nuclear-free zones and so on.

The basic facts about the bomb and its use are harsh and terrifying for civilization; they have become lost in a mass of theoretical verbiage. It has been said that the world has learned to live with the bomb. But in the words of one editorial writer, there is no need for it to drift unnecessarily into the position that it is prepared to die for it.

The ultimate point of reason for the world to decide—and this applies both to nuclear and nonnuclear powers—is what short-term interests it is prepared to sacrifice in this nuclear age in exchange for long-term survival and security.

4

Through the Crystal Ball

MY AIM IN THE PRECEDING THREE CHAPTERS WAS TO UNRAVEL some of the past, and to indicate certain trends which characterize the present interaction of science and military affairs. In this chapter I take my courage in both hands and look to the future. How is it all going to work out?

I cannot even begin to emulate the prophetic vision of a Leonardo, who was able to conceive of flying machines heavier than air four hundred years before the development of the internal combustion engine made it possible for anything of the kind he had in mind to take wing. In our own days of fast-moving science, anyone who speculates about the nature and impact of future technical developments does so at his peril. It is now only thirty-three years to the year 2000. One might imagine this is not too long a period over which to hazard a guess, at least in general terms, of the ways along which science is likely to progress, and affect social and political relations. But were I to put myself in the position of a speaker of thirty-three years ago, I am certain that I should not have foreseen—and I doubt whether anyone did foresee—the tremendous changes which would occur within science and which science would bring about in society in what to many of us seems only a very short span of time.

Who, in 1930, could have conceived that the intervening years would witness the flowering of nuclear physics; the discoveries of the new science of radio astronomy; the emergence of

a new world of molecular biology; amazing advances in medicine
ranging from the discovery and exploitation of antibiotics to, say,
the arterial-transplantation techniques of surgery; the birth and
development of radar; the discovery of the transistor and the
range of uses to which it has been put; the jet engine and its
influence both within and outside the field of aeronautics; or the
amazing developments in space which have already falsified
authoritative predictions made only a few years back that the
other side of the moon would never be known to man? And who
could have imagined that vast parts of our metropolitan civilization would become so dependent upon electrical power that, as
was dramatically demonstrated in the northeast of the United
States a short time back, its withdrawal would mean all but the
total paralysis of social life in a major part of that vast and rich
country? Or who, in 1930, could have foreseen that the multiplication of motorcars would lead, in less than forty years, to a
situation in which we face the stark alternatives of either a complete redesign of our city centers, or a major limitation of road
traffic, or inevitable self-imposed chaos? The list of yesterday's
technical touchstones seems endless, and yet in 1930 hardly one
of them was more than the rudiment of a possibility, and most
of them were not even that.

Looking back to 1930, I can see two important general reasons
why any speaker of that day would have found his scientific and
political predictions falsified by events. First, he would never
have guessed that science was soon to be supported—whatever
the reasons—on the scale we have come to accept as normal
today. And, second, he would hardly have been rash enough to
depart from the opinions which were then generally held about
the likely trends in the growth of population in the United
Kingdom and in the world as a whole.[1] Even as late as 1949, a
Royal Commission[2] reporting on population growth in the
United Kingdom "confidently" predicted that there was going
to be a "substantial decline in the annual number of births over
the next fifteen years." In fact, the number has increased over
this period by nearly 50 percent. Today we are only too well

aware that one of the major factors which is going to shape our own future and that of the world is the so-called "population explosion."

Today I am, at least, helped in any predictions I might make because I am aware of these developments. But even so, I am not going to risk a forty-year look. I propose to remain on safer ground and to restrict my prophecies about the mutual interaction of science and military affairs to, say, the end of the 1970s, a period of some fifteen years ahead. This is not only a more sensible time scale for the international political stage, but also a period which is already constrained, to some extent at least, by certain immutable trends. The first of these derives from the increasing sophistication of defense research and development. The price of putting science and technology to work to produce ever more complicated weapons and military equipment is becoming so high, as I pointed out in the second chapter, that even the United States, the richest country in the world—and, therefore, one presumes, the U.S.S.R. as well—is beginning to feel the pinch. I shall return to this point later. The second constraint derived from the fact that the successful development from drawing board to finished article of any new sophisticated weapon system a new aircraft or a new guided weapon—rarely takes less than seven years, and more often ten. It is now the beginning of 1967. Practically none of the new major weapon systems of whose development the world knows —for example, variable-sweep supersonic aircraft—could be of much operational significance until the early 1970s. Those that are not already in at least the early stages of design could hardly affect the relative strengths of the great military powers before the 1980s. More than a little can happen in the political "lineup" between now and then.

The third consideration which eases the task of what I might call "midterm prediction" is the fact that with the attention which is paid in these days to weapons of war, there is probably no known scientific principle that has not already been carefully scrutinized to see whether it is of any significance for defense.

This examination has embraced the principles which have led to the production of what are called "clean"* nuclear weapons; of "Rip van Winkle"† gases, designed to immobilize an enemy rather than to kill him; of infrared sensors; of automatic reconnaissance systems; of communications based on lasers‡ and so on. It would be in the highest degree unlikely—although, of course, not impossible—if the search for military advantage, on the scale pursued in the U.S.A. and the U.S.S.R., had overlooked any potential application of an established piece of scientific knowledge. It is all but inconceivable, therefore, that we shall see any radical change in, say, the next ten years which can be attributed to the further exploitation of known science. Even more remote are the changes which might follow the exploitation of scientific principles and effects that are yet to be discovered. No one can build on the unknown.

The fourth consideration which will undoubtedly have a major effect upon the mutual impact of science and military affairs is that the two do not interact *in vacuo*, but within a world landscape in which social and economic problems and

* *Clean weapons:* The energy in a nuclear explosion can be obtained either from the fission of atoms of suitable heavy elements or from the fusion of atoms of light elements. In both cases the process is accompanied by the formation of radioactive elements, but the amount of radioactivity produced in the fusion process is less than that produced in fission. Clean weapons are those in which a deliberate attempt has been made, by relying as far as possible on the fusion process, to reduce the amount of radio activity produced.

† *Rip van Winkle gas:* Originally, research on chemical agents to be used in warfare was concentrated on those agents which could kill or seriously injure. Later research resulted in nonlethal agents, of which tear gas is probably the best known example, which were designed not to injure but merely to incapacitate for a short period of time. Modern work has suggested the possibility of agents which change the victim's mental outlook—one well-publicized discovery, for example, has been an agent which makes cats terrified of mice. Work such as this suggests that the way may be opening to a class of agents that inflicts no permanent damage but which removes from the enemy all warlike "drive."

‡ *Lasers:* The light from most sources (e.g., the sun, electric lights, etc.) is built up from the contributions of innumerable radiating atoms, each producing its light quite independently of the rest. In the laser (*Light Amplification by Stimulated Emission of Radiation*) a method has been found of coordinating the individual atomic sources so that all radiate in phase and all produce light of the same wavelength. The light produced from the laser has exceptional properties, one of which is that a beam, once formed, spreads scarcely at all.

political relationships are being rapidly transformed. These changes are occurring faster than the kind of technological developments which, for example, "put paid" to the fabulously expensive antiaircraft system SAGE even before it was ready to be deployed. The fact of political change is immensely important when one tries to see what the world of military power could be like ten, twenty years ahead. And the force and direction of some of the more potent winds of change which are transforming the world scene are there for all to see.

Anyone who wishes to speculate about the ways science and military affairs will interact in the future must take into account not only the limits of scientific possibility, but also these four sets of considerations. With them in mind it seems to me reasonable to make two quite general predictions about the nature of the immediate future which faces us. The first is that the changes which could be attributed to the direct impact of science on military affairs will be less important than those which stem from political transformations. And the second is that science itself will accelerate these political changes less because of its direct influence on the military machine than because of its effects on social and political life in general.

The Cost of Technology in Relation to the Arms Race

Let me examine in more detail the constraints that aid me in my task of predicting over a fifteen-year period. First, I turn again to the rising cost of modern technology, the subject I discussed in Chapter 2. An arms race is a race that has no finishing post. There is no absolute goal—there is no end to demand. There is no ultimate military weapon. Do we ask for more destructive power? Then the enemy "hardens" his targets, or changes his tactics. Do we ask for another missile that is so designed that it can seek and "home" on its target? Then the enemy alters the size of the target, or suppresses the telltale signals to which the sensors of the missile respond, or gives the target greater mobility. The process is circular, and each forward

step can be taken only by applying the results of scientific and
technological advances, which are increasingly difficult to come
by. The easy steps have all been taken—only the most difficult
remain. And these steps are, without exception, the most expensive.

It is this which has led to the trend of ever-rising costs in
defense research and development, a trend which cannot fail to
be one of the main controls that govern the future shape and
size of our armed forces. If, to repeat the steps of the argument,
a country wishes its forces to be armed in the most up-to-date
way possible, then it must reequip them at frequent intervals
with weapons and other equipment—radars, aircraft, ships—
more complicated and more expensive than those that are replaced. Unless an ever-increasing proportion of a country's
G.N.P. is devoted to defense, or an increasing proportion of its
defense budget is devoted to research and development—and
these alternatives are unlikely to commend themselves to governments on the one hand, or to generals on the other—forces
must become smaller in numbers, or commitments must be cut
so that the need for introducing some of the most expensive new
weapons can be avoided. For this main reason each new military
demand must be most searchingly scrutinized and evaluated if
we are not to go on being dogged by the expensive cancellations
which have been so prominent a feature of recent history. That
the necessity for this scrutiny applies as much to the superpowers as it does to the U.K. was well illustrated by a Congressional debate which took place some three years ago about the
relative merits of propelling naval vessels by nuclear or conventional power.[3]

Mr. Robert McNamara, the American Secretary of Defense,
in defending the proposition that conventionally powered
vessels were not only cheaper but also adequate from the point
of view of the job that needed to be done, outlined his position
in the following words.

Consider, he said—I quote his own words—the farmer who
has "a requirement for moving a certain quantity of grain to

town. He has a truck that meets that requirement. It happens to move at thirty miles an hour and has these other characteristics.

"Someone else comes along and says I have a better truck. It will move at eighty miles an hour. You ought to have the best. Your farm and you deserve nothing but the best. But he says I don't need the other fifty miles an hour. My grain is moved.

"I therefore should not spend the money on that. There is no ceiling on expenditures for trucks. He has to move the grain. He would pay twice as much as the thirty-mile-an-hour truck cost, he would not lose his harvest by not doing so. But he doesn't need to pay any more. His grain is moved." In falling back on this analogy Mr. McNamara was not questioning the proposition that nuclear-powered vessels were technically better, ship for ship, than those propelled by conventional engines. Neither was he, one imagines, trying to stop the march of technology. What he was questioning was the assumption that the greater cost of the nuclear-powered vessel would be justified by a strengthening of the position of the U.S.A. relative to that of the U.S.S.R. He was operating on the general proposition that while science is itself responsible for the machinery or method which provides it with its authority, the directions of technology, to quote Admiral Rickover again,[4] are properly a subject of debate, not alone by experts, but by the public as well.

There can be no need for me to develop this point further. The consequences of the ever-increasing costs of technological sophistication—at least in the open societies of the West—are plain for all to see in the cancellations of vastly expensive projects, such as TSR-2 or Skybolt, that have already taken place. The important point is that these cancellations have occurred not only in what I might call "middle-class" powers, such as the U.K. and Canada—for whom the pace of the race is dictated by the runners in the lead—but also in the U.S.A. and, one imagines, in the U.S.S.R. as well.

All countries engaged in the modern arms race are playing for the same high stakes at the same table. Each fears that a rival may gain a lead in applying the most advanced scientific knowl-

edge and technology to the development and production of a
new sophisticated weapon system. The U.S. Department of
Defense, which has been spending on average about six billion
dollars a year on research and development over the past few
years, has already discovered that it is impossible to cover, even
with the vast resources made available to it, including technical
manpower, the whole field of development in which the armed
services wish to be concerned in their efforts to keep their
armory absolutely up to date. If today's emphasis on technological preparations for defense were to continue for many more
years, research and development could, in theory, consume all
the resources available to the U.S. government for all forms of
social expenditure. I am told that some scientific schemes that
have been dreamed up in the civil field could do the same.

For this reason various authorities in the U.S.A. are already
examining the problem of how to control the growth rate of
what is now familiarly called "big science," and it has already
been decided to try to help redress the balance of scientific effort
by awarding grants and contracts to institutes not already heavily
engaged in Federal Research Programs.[5] No doubt financial
controls will follow, in the same way as we in the U.K. already
have had to limit the proportion of public money that can be
made available for science. The painful lessons we have learned
in defense research are also now being learned in the United
States.

The Consequences for Cooperation

Where has this technological defense race led? The first major
consequence has been the appearance of a widening gap between two superpowers on the one hand, and the remaining
nations of the world on the other. And the United Kingdom is
among these other nations. The effects of expensive living—with
nations as well as with individuals—is felt first by those with
small and relatively fixed incomes.

The second major consequence—a result of the fact that up

to the present the two superpowers have been able to deploy enough effort to dig equally deeply in the treasure house of science and technology—is that the U.S.A. and U.S.S.R. are in a mutual state of scientific, technological and military stalemate.

The third major consequence—which is illustrated by the course of the "low level" wars which we have seen in the past ten or fifteen years, Korea and Vietnam for example,—is that the leading powers are not, on the whole, well equipped to fight the sort of war with which we are now becoming familiar. Growing expense and closely regulated budgets have imposed a need for choice; the choice has been, in most cases, for the highly sophisticated, highly destructive weapon systems; some possibilities which have gone by the board are those which now, it appears, would have been the most useful.

What of the future? It seems to me that with the world as it is, the "inexorable law" of the rising cost of technological sophistication will lead to a still wider gap than already exists between industrialized countries on the one hand and underdeveloped and newly industrializing countries on the other. A country with a limited G.N.P. which decides that it must devote a large proportion of its resources to the maintenance of standing military forces, to the purchase of foreign arms and equipment, and to the inevitable and consequential development of its own organization for defense research, technology and development, is unlikely to have much to spare for less glamorous, but more important, tasks of strengthening and expanding the industrial foundations of prosperity and power.

The future will, of course, see increasing efforts by all countries whose resources are being strained by the ever-rising costs of military power, including the United States, to alleviate their difficulties through the standardization of weapons and equipment, and by cooperation in research and development. Standardization is a need which has long been recognized within the Western Alliance. The rationale of this step is the simple proposition that it is both more effective operationally and cheaper all round for allies to be armed with the same weapons.

But strangely enough, standardization has proved very difficult to achieve, and has so far succeeded only in relatively small fields of equipment. National habits and prejudices die hard. All countries seem to believe that what they design and develop is better than the corresponding things made elsewhere.

International cooperation in research and development, to which I referred in Chapter 2, now appears to be a course on which the United Kingdom, after many a false start, is truly launched. Beginning only about three years ago, we are now cooperating in the development of expensive weapon systems with France, Western Germany and the United States. This form of mutual help is important and historically significant not only because it spreads the cost of expensive development and leads to standardization, but because the scale of the projects, in terms of resources committed, are relatively so enormous that their execution demands the most intimate and personal technical and industrial liaison between countries. The international industrial agreements which are defined through advanced technology may, therefore, have far-reaching political consequences. It is, of course, not only "big science" in the defense field which has led to this form of international cooperation. The European Launcher Development and the European Space Research Organizations, like the European Center for Nuclear Research, are illustrations of the same process at work in fields of civil science.

It is a paradoxical thought that while science and technology are brought to bear on military affairs in the hope that increased military power helps ensure national independence, all Western industrial powers, in trying to lessen the costs of the process, are being forced into an increasing degree of mutual understanding and cooperation. Scientists have always known that there are no national barriers to basic scientific knowledge; that science is an international, a nonnational force. The world at large is now learning that the exploitation of scientific and technical knowledge is also a process which can lead to political understanding and a lowering of international barriers. The differential rate at which scientific knowledge has been exploited over the past two to three decades has helped transform power relationships—look at the change in world status of the U.K., of the U.S.A. and of the U.S.S.R. Who can tell what further changes are possible?

The Applications of New Science

One might well ask, with the examples of new scientific wonders which I listed at the beginning of this chapter in mind, whether any new science, as such, is likely to affect the military balance of the great powers over the next fifteen years. My own answer to this question would, in general, even if hesitatingly, be "No." As I have said, nothing that is not already in the pipeline of development of military equipment can have much significant effect on the balance of power for years to come; and all principles known to science have already been closely scrutinized for their possible applications to defense. The massive programs of work on lasers, which are now going on all over the world, may well bear fruit both in the field of communications and in that of weapons. But I do not see them generating a new technical dimension in military affairs. Nor can I see developments in the fields of bacteriological and chemical warfare making any decisive change in the strategic balance between the great powers. Above all, I cannot see how any further developments in sophisticated weapons technology on which the great powers might embark could make much difference to the kind of wars with which the world has become familiar over the past twenty years —Korea, Indochina, Malaya, the Congo and Vietnam—or to the kind of nuclear scenario which is already too terrible for civilization to contemplate.

Computers

But I must qualify this prediction. There is one development of modern technology which, within the next ten years, could have a profound effect on the way that defense is controlled. I

refer to computers. I say this as an act of faith. We all believe
that computers are a "good thing," even though we cannot yet
see clearly either how far they can be developed or what the
consequences of their development will be.

What we do know is that computers have an almost limitless
ability to absorb, store and process information, and that this
may well have a profound effect on military operations and upon
the control of the military machine in general, as it already has
over the working of particular weapons, such as ballistic missiles.
There are obvious areas where computers can take over jobs
done at "middle-management" levels which, till now, have been
manned by specialist officers. Typical of such areas would be
those which concern the "general housekeeping" of a service—
for example, the calculation and issue of the soldier's pay or the
control of the whole complex of stores. One can already envisage
computer-controlled machines automatically "ordering" spares
to be sent to distant depots as stocks reach critically low levels,
or even calling for replacements from the producers.

There is another application of computer technology which
could also be of particular use to the military. By setting up
"models" or "simulations" of battle, we can, with the aid of
high-speed computers, examine not only the interaction of many
variables but also repeat the process many times to display the
full spectrum of possible results and their relative likelihood. This
offers a powerful method of coming to grips with certain of the
problems defense planners face—how to get the most security
for a given expenditure. There are, of course, considerable difficulties in defining or measuring the term "security." In the business world, success is judged mainly by profits, or by the volume
of turnover. These straightforward measures have no meaning in
the world of defense. No definition of effectiveness can be
formulated in any formal sense, particularly in the tactical arena,
and the only measure of "profits" that could have any meaning
is the avoidance of defeat and the achievement of victory, given
one is in a war, or the avoidance of war through a variety of

measures, of which the deterrent value of one's armory of weapons is only one.

Perhaps of greater interest is the possibility, even if a remote possibility, that a combination of computers and rapid communications could put distant military operations under immediate central control. We are already at the stage when London or Washington could know within minutes as much about the detail of some military operation on the far side of the world as would the local commander in chief, who, paradoxically, might not know as much as would, say, the battalion commanders in the field. This being the case, it is not out of the question that the next step will be that the commander on the spot will be receiving instructions about his next actions from the central government. Science, by magnifying the destructiveness of modern war, has created the need for this kind of central control; and it has also provided the means whereby the need can be met.

It is difficult to see what effect this possible development could have on the calling of "generalship," on the qualities required for men in senior military positions, or on the attractions of military life as a career. But there is bound to be some effect, and it may be a profound one. This aspect of the social consequences of computers is of fairly general significance. As in the military sphere, computers are tending to substitute for "middle management" in the industrial and commercial world, and are thus tending to increase the gulf between the top-level decision-makers and the men who still do things on the shop floor. In neither case do we know how the widening gulf is going to be bridged.

Apart from what may flow from the increasing use that is being made of computers, I feel fairly sure, for the reasons I have already given, that the battlefield of the next ten years or so is not likely to be affected significantly by any new applications of science. Professor Rabi,[6] the eminent American physicist who has maintained close links with military science ever since the early 1940s, and who contributed greatly to the development of microwave radar,* shares this view. He reminds us that we are now past the peak of exploitation of the great scientific developments of the last century, and that the discoveries which might mean much for the future are still outside the field of practical and even military application. He also tells us that the concept of the laser was clearly foreshadowed in a paper published by Einstein in 1917, but that it took forty years before the idea was exploited, in spite of the fact that, in Professor Rabi's view, the basic principle is simpler than those on which radar or television are based. His views reassure me when I say that I foresee nothing as revolutionary as radar, nuclear weapons and nuclear power, guided weapons and ballistic missiles, communication satellites, or high-speed computers emerging over the next ten, fifteen years.

So much for my predictions about the further changes which might result from the direct application of new science to military affairs. To sum up, I see no change occurring in the balance of strategic military power—more precisely destructive power—between the Western and Soviet blocs. I see the persistence of a technological stalemate, with the ever-increasing cost of advanced technology as the major controlling factor; I see an increasing disparity between the industrial and the developing nations; and I see, paradoxically, tension lessening and closer international cooperation between nations which are already highly industrialized.

Population Changes

So far, my task as prophet has seemed relatively easy, or at least—since I have confined myself to the direct interaction of

* *Microwave radar:* The original radars of the Second World War used radio waves of which the wavelength was about five meters. The shorter the wavelength used, the easier it is to form a narrow beam and the smaller the transmitting and receiving aerials can be. Microwave radar, which is now used extensively in airborne applications, employs wavelengths of between one and ten centimeters.

science and military affairs—I have made it easy by covering a relatively limited field, and then over a relatively short span of years. I turn now to possible changes in the political and social matrix of military power which are likely to transform its emphasis over the years ahead. And here my task becomes more difficult. An important—and from the seer's point of view, frustrating—aspect of social and political change is that it can be relatively sudden in its impact. As I have already said, we have only to look at our relations with Communist Russia and with Germany to see this—as we stand at present, yesterday's opponent and ally have changed places. The dice are heavily loaded against the military prophet when his predictions have to take into account not only the march of science, but also seemingly capricious, and often rapid, changes in his political frame of reference.

Although we may not be able to envisage the actual social and political changes which are likely to occur in our own country, we can recognize the social forces that, without doubt, are bringing about change. Of these probably the most significant single one which is now conditioning the course of world events, and so our own place in the world, is the so-called population explosion. The population of the world today is about 3,300 million. By the year 2000 A.D. it could reach, on the basis of present trends, nearly 7,000 million (a figure ten times that of 1750). Not only are the numbers of people multiplying fast; the rate of increase is also accelerating. World population about doubled in the hundred years which ended with 1950. The present doubling period could be only fifty years. Clearly this enormous rate of increase will have profound political and economic repercussions, which will be acutely conditioned by the fact that the rate is not the same everywhere. It is highest—I take up this point below—in the underdeveloped parts of the world and lowest in Europe.

It would be folly to brush these numerical omens aside; all experience shows that rates of population increase have always been under-, not overestimated in recent years. Growth rates can, of course, change abruptly, and they can go down as well as up. But over the past twenty-five years they have, in general, remained disturbingly high.

We can get some "feel" for the scale of the population changes which the future may bring if we use the latest figures for rates of increase in different countries, as given by the United Nations Population Bureau,[7] in order to derive estimates of population size about the year 1980. I have restricted the sums to a few countries only, and have "rounded" the figures on the lower side.

	Present Population (millions)	1980 Population (millions)	Increase (millions)
U.K.	52	59	7
U.S.A.	189	248	59
Australia	10	14	4
New Zealand	2	3	1
India	460	600–650	? 150
Pakistan	98	140	40
Malaysia	10	17	7
Indonesia	100	145	45
Egypt	28	42	14
Japan	98	110	12
U.S.S.R.	224	275	51
China	654	1,000+	? 350

Throughout the world the accelerated growth of population is indirectly due to the interaction, in varying measure, of improvements in health on the one hand, and developments in agriculture and industry on the other. The primary direct cause is that human beings are now enjoying a greater span of reproductive life because of a general decline in infantile mortality, and an increase in the expectation of life resulting from such measures as the elimination of malaria by D.D.T., improvements in hygiene and sanitary techniques, and the introduction of antibiotics. Man has eliminated some diseases and reduced the incidence and severity of others. In Ceylon, to quote an extreme and well-known illustration, the death rate in the seven-year period 1945 to 1952 fell from 22 to 12 per thousand mainly because of the elimination of the malaria mosquito by D.D.T. spraying.

It took seventy years of the nineteenth and early part of this century to achieve a corresponding fall in the United Kingdom. In the single year 1946 to 1947, the death rate in Ceylon fell from 20 to 14 per thousand.

Food Production

Improvements in agriculture, brought about by better husbandry, mechanization and the introduction of herbicides and pesticides, have helped to provide food for the world's growing populations—but not enough. According to a recent report of the Food and Agriculture Organization,[8] nearly three–quarters of the world's population still lack sufficient food, and hundreds of millions are still starving. The shortage is particularly bad in Asia, where over half of the world's population lives. Furthermore, improvements in food supply in some of the underdeveloped countries have in turn accelerated the rate of population growth.

The world shortage of food is already acute, and the way things are going it is difficult not to see it getting worse. The average rise in total world food production has been less than one percent per annum over the last decade, and the increase has been lowest in countries where it was most needed. In the Far East the figure was less than 0.4 percent; in North America it exceeded 2 percent. If we look ahead only as far as 1980, the average increase for the world as a whole should be about 2¼ percent if it is to match the average growth of population. Rates higher than average are called for in underdeveloped countries, both because their present populations are undernourished and because it is in these countries that population is growing most rapidly. National disparities in food requirements and food production can only be marginally affected by international trade, except in cases such as our own. As an industrialized nation, England is fortunate to be able to buy from abroad, mainly out of the proceeds of the overseas sales of manufactured goods, half the food, and most of the protein, which the country consumes.

The crystal ball clearly warns that national differences in population density and in rates of population growth, as well as in supplies of food and other raw materials, are likely to be greater as we approach the turn of the century than they are today—and that they will increase even if new measures of birth control become effective in countries like India and China. If these measures fail, the differences could well be catastrophic. That is one reason why a solution to the problem of birth control is so critical for the future of the world. Whether the possibilities of synthetic food production will be realized in time remains to be seen. The technical problems are immense, and their solution is hardly aided by the innate conservatism of our food habits,[9] which have changed relatively little since Neolithic times.

Communications, Education and Propaganda

Differences in the political relations of the nations of the world will also be powerfully influenced by the increasing speed with which knowledge and propaganda can now be disseminated. The exploitation of science has led to various powerful new methods of mass communication—particularly radio and, to a lesser extent, television—and mass communications have exposed the world to the world. Most underdeveloped nations now have a clear realization of their plight, and have become persuaded that oppression and starvation are not the natural heritage of mankind. This belief has contributed in large measure to the end of colonialism and to the multiplication of sovereign nations. When a country begins to feel that it is being downtrodden and deprived, it automatically assumes that life would be better were it left to its own devices. Whether or not events justify the assumption is neither here nor there. The grass is always greener on the other side of the fence, and risks will always be taken for freedom and independence.

The Future

Behind all this lies the hand of science. Its applications have led to burgeoning populations, to a rapidly spreading awareness of the maldistribution of the world's resources, including knowledge, and so to political unrest. The big question is whether all this will intensify, or whether some other advances of science could pour oil on the troubled waters brought about by differential population growth and by the uneven distribution of resources. I find it difficult to be optimistic.

My disquiet arises primarily from the fact that population is growing at very different rates in the world. As I have already pointed out, we expect population in the U.K. to increase by about 7 millions between now and 1980—that is to say, to increase by a little more than 10 percent. In the same period, the population of the U.S.A. could increase by about 25 percent, i.e., by about 60 million people. But the increase in India, over the period, could on present trends be well over 100 million; in Pakistan 40 million, in Malaysia 7 million; in Indonesia 45 million. And in mainland China the 1980 population could well be around 1,000 million, an increase of 300–400 million. No one need suppose that these are cast-iron figures, but the broad lines of the picture which they define cannot be ignored. With few exceptions population is growing fastest in those countries which one would have thought had the most to gain by the reverse trend, and is lowest in those where restraint seems least needed.

In theory the twin problems of population and food can be solved. We are not lacking the scientific knowledge which would make this possible. But the problem is formidable since its solution depends mainly on social, political and economic factors. Without stable governments able to develop and impose long-term educational and economic plans, and able to give the plans the overriding priority they will need, we shall get nowhere. The solution depends everywhere upon the intelligent cooperation of a country's people as a whole. And for this, educational levels will have to rise well above present standards in most parts of the world. The task of bridging the gap, in a single generation, between the level of education that is appropriate to an industrial age and the virtually Stone Age conditions which still exist in some countries is a daunting one. Parts of New Guinea are almost untouched by civilization. In countries such as Malawi and Ethiopia again only between 1 percent and 2 percent of children of secondary-school age are at school. There is, as Professors Harbison and Meyers[10] have shown, a close association between education and G.N.P. In Nigeria, where the per-capita annual income is equivalent to 64 United States dollars, less than one person in a thousand has had twelve or more years' schooling. In the United States, by contrast, where the average income is 2,800 dollars a year, this period of schooling has been surpassed by nearly 300 people in every thousand. In the field of education, as almost everywhere else, the cards are heavily stacked against the underdeveloped nations.

Even if countries uneducated in the ways of modern technology succeed in producing a corps of technicians, let alone highly qualified scientists and engineers, they still have the problem of integrating them into the community and government machine, and of discouraging their departure to countries offering greater opportunities for the exercise of their talents and skills. The great educational gap between a comparatively few elite and the masses also has its dangers, since there is little basis for dialogue between peoples of different attainments. Political stability is hard to achieve in these circumstances.

I have said enough to indicate why I expect that there will be widespread political change over the next few decades, and why I fear that political unrest may increase rather than decrease in the years ahead of us. The most significant implication of the figures I have quoted is the likelihood that the focus of social and economic pressure, and consequently of political change, will for some time continue to be China and the neighboring countries of the Far East. We know that China is now increasing her industrial power, and we know, too, that she is devoting scarce resources to building up her armed forces. She has already embarked on the highly expensive and dangerous course of devising a nuclear arsenal. With a population of around seven hundred million, she is already a major figure on the world scene—how much more important an influence will she become when her population has increased by yet another hundred million or two? Fortunately, the Chinese Communist Party have themselves become alarmed by the prospect of uninhibited population growth. We are now told that the intention is to stabilize the population "well below" the thousand million mark. To this end, Edgar Snow[11] writes, "efforts to limit births are being intensified in perhaps the most thoroughgoing program yet to be *officially* sponsored by any nation."

Conclusion

It is not my business to pursue a political analysis. I have said what I have said in order to illustrate the proposition that, in my view, military affairs are likely to be affected in the years ahead less by the direct impact of science, for example, on various fields of weapon development, than by the changes which are being brought about both directly and indirectly in the political arena. As I see it, the political relations of the industrialized countries of the world are altering not only because of the rising cost of science and technology, and in particular because of the strains associated with the race to develop ever more sophisticated weapon systems; they are also being transformed because of the political pressures brought about by the population and resources crisis of the world. Political unrest due to social, economic and other pressures stemming indirectly from scientific advances is intensifying in underdeveloped countries, and this very unrest is helping to define and consolidate the interests of all the industrial powers in the preservation of world peace.

All nations, both the "haves" and the "have-nots," are directly concerned with the problem of high rates of growth of population, and with the disparity between human numbers and the availability of food. Even the most prosperous countries do not have unlimited wealth. They do not have resources sufficient to keep up the pace of the arms race, as it has been set in recent years, at the same time as they foster major developments in the civil sphere and provide "technical aid" for underdeveloped territories. A few years ago civil "fallout" was a respectable excuse for growing defense research and development budgets. But today no one would deny that the insistent call made by the military machine upon the research and development resources of industrialized countries holds back progress in other fields of national activity. And no one would urge that modern technological industry, for example the electronics industry, is so dependent upon progress in defense research and development that it could not thrive except on the basis of military "fallout"; to argue, for example, that there would have been no television without radar, no nuclear power if there had not been research on nuclear weapons. Technological and industrial progress can certainly be ensured by more direct methods.

Science and technology have not only changed the structure and nature of the military machine. They have also transformed the arena within which armies, navies and air forces are to be seen as instruments of political power. Clausewitz's doctrine that "war is a continuation of political exchanges by other means" has no sense in a nuclear age. The military emphasis has now shifted from big wars to little ones; the focus of political attention from the Western hemisphere to the Eastern. The changes are there for all to see. They have occurred mainly through the development and spread of new technologies, which in their wake have brought new problems to press on the world. These can and will be solved, but only by a conscious determination on the part of all nations to use science as future generations would commend.

5

Priorities and Secrecy in Science

SCIENCE, AS WE KNOW IT TODAY, IS A CULTURAL PRODUCT OF medieval Western Europe. Why it should have been that the particular system of scientific method which has proved so successful, and which has swept the world in a way no single religious or political system has ever done, should have emerged in the seventeenth century rather than in some earlier age, and in Western Europe rather than in, say, China or Greece or some corner of Islam, is a matter for speculation. Unlike what happened in Europe, it may have been, as many have suggested, that the emergence of the urban civilizations of these other parts of the world was associated with a diversification of labor which led to an unfortunate separation of the craftsmen out of whose labors man's earliest views of science were born, from a specialized class of privileged philosophers and priests who were not concerned with the actual doing of things.

Be this as it may, our kind of scientific environment, an environment of experiment and controlled observation, emerged in a sparsely populated Europe, in which illiteracy was the rule rather than the exception, and in which the Galileos and Newtons, the Leonardos and the Wrens, as well as the informed princes and merchants to whose society they belonged, were not only interested in the advance of pure knowledge, but generally conscious of the fact that material riches and power followed in the train of science. As Christopher Wren put it in a draft constitution which he drew up in 1660 as the basis for Charles II's

prospective Charter for the Royal Society, the purpose of the
members of such a Society should be to "prosecute effectually
the Advancement of Natural Experimental Philosophy, especially those Parts of it which concern the Encrease of Commerce, by the Addition of Useful Inventions tending to the
Ease, Profit, or Health of our Subjects."[1]

The fathers of modern science saw science as a body of exact
knowledge which could lead to useful application, and as we
would call it today, technology. But their successors did not
always view it in the same light. In the United Kingdom, for
example, pure science has in general flourished over the years,
whereas scientific technology has only too often languished. In
other countries, notably the United States and Germany, the
importance and value of an up-to-date technology has always
been widely recognized. Whenever efforts have been made to
spur the United Kingdom to an interest in science and in education in the sciences, as happened during a large part of the
nineteenth century, and as has been going on continuously
during the two decades since the Second World War, attention
has been directed, for purposes of example, to the achievements
of other nations, and the emphasis of the debate has been essentially utilitarian. There was as much talk of the need for more
science in nineteenth-century England, with commissions coun-
seling the establishment of Ministries of Science and of Government Boards of Science, as there can have been anywhere in the
world. Perhaps the most powerful propagandist for science of
modern times was Lyon Playfair, who warned his fellow Brit-
ishers as early as 1851 that "as surely as darkness follows the
setting of the sun, so surely will England recede as a manufacturing nation, unless her industrial population becomes much more
conversant with science than they now are."[2] And a little later
he added: "In this country we have eminent 'practical' men and
eminent 'scientific' men, but they are not united and generally
walk in paths wholly distinct. . . . From this absence of connection there is often a want of mutual esteem and a misappre-
hension of their relative importance to each other."

Scientists Today

But whatever differences there may have been in the scientific histories of different countries, and whatever the routes whereby they have made their way into the present age, and to the enjoyment of what has become a common scientific heritage, all scientists since the Second World War now find themselves in much the same position—prime actors in a new dynamic phase of the world's social and political evolution. Those who belonged to countries which were involved in the war found themselves part of the most determined and directed drive to gain and harness scientific knowledge that the world had ever known, and supported on a scale which made the cumulative total of the resources that in previous decades had gone to science seem trivial. The immediate results, as we all know, were the emergence of radar, jet engines, penicillin, the atom bomb, D.D.T. and a host of other things.

The secondary results of this harnessing of science were as numerous, and in some ways more important to the future of the world. The demand in which scientists and engineers found themselves twenty-five years ago has not only continued, but has spread to all countries. There can never have been a period in history when any other profession has been so universally cultivated. All countries, old and new, have had to expand and improve their facilities for higher education and, in particular, for scientific education. The size of the full-time university population of the United Kingdom has tripled in the past twenty years, and postgraduate education has multiplied even more—yet the call for more scientific manpower seems as insistent now as it was when it all began. In all industrialized countries, too, financial support for science and engineering, instead of falling back to prewar levels, is now far higher than it has ever been. The 20 billion or so dollars available for research and development in the United States compares with some 3 billion in 1946 and the 750 million pounds in the United

Kingdom with 70 million—a vast difference even after allowing for the effects of inflation, and for increases in our numbers.

Increasing numbers of scientists and engineers, and increasing support for research and development, constitute what one might describe as an intrinsic aspect of the new wave of technological exploitation which is now engulfing the world. Its external aspect is made up of those divergent forces which lead to the ever-mounting demand for more science and technology: more science to assure better health or better measures of birth control; more agricultural science to improve agricultural output in impoverished parts of the world; more research and development for weapon systems; more resources for space science and satellite communications; a better scientific outlook to improve transportation and other public services—and in the private sphere the host of innovations which are always welcomed by the ordinary consumer. In a period of violent and rapid transformation, everyone looks to "science" for a more secure and a happier future.

The Scientist at His Bench

This tidal wave of interest in science has made little difference to the nature of the individual research worker. Usually we still see him growing up in a university department where his first field of inquiry would have been greatly influenced by the work, however narrow or however wide its intellectual scope, that was going on around him. To some extent, he, therefore, begins as a victim of fashion, in the same way as did his teachers before him; and to an extent which will vary with his own powers, and particularly with his capacity for truly original thinking, he will continue as such, if he carries on as a research worker at all. A far-reaching advance in the laboratory in which he may be working, whether it happens to be in his own or in a related field of interest, may turn the direction of his inquiries. So, too, will some new major development in another laboratory.

He can be expected to demand conditions which will allow

him to proceed as fast as his inspiration impels, and in the direction it commands. He cannot predict when success will crown his efforts. A lot of his work will turn out to be plain hard slogging—but no less fascinating for that—whether he is researching in some esoteric branch of natural knowledge, or directing his energies to advancing some obviously utilitarian field of applied science. What he basically wants and needs is the assurance that he will be allowed to give full rein to his curiosity without being harried, until the moment comes when he himself thinks his ideas have either flowered or run into the sands, and it is time to change direction, or give up research. He wants a library and journals in which to publish. He wants an environment in which there are no bars to the acquisition of the knowledge gained by others. He needs the opportunity to discuss, at scientific meetings and seminars, mutual interests with colleagues. When appropriate, he would like guidance and encouragement, and when he discovers something new, the acclaim of colleagues—there have been very few scientists who have wished to remain anonymous, or to suppress the discoveries which they have made. Every scientist is a member of a worldwide community of scientists, all of whom work in the same field. The "community" may sometimes consist of no more than a half-dozen men; sometimes it may number hundreds or even thousands. But whatever its size, it constitutes the particular intellectual environment in which the scientist exercises his specialty, and where basically he seeks to be recognized and judged.

Whether a scientific discovery proves to be far-reaching or trivial, it is inevitably an act of creation. What matters to the scientist, as Koestler[3] so eloquently puts it, is "the emergence of order out of disorder, of signal out of noise, of harmony out of dissonance, of a meaningful whole out of meaningless bits, of cosmos out of chaos." Few can enjoy this kind of revelation— which indeed applies to any field of creative activity—or derive from it any sense of fulfillment, without trying to communicate it to others. This is so even though communication is not inevitably associated with acceptance. Something which is new is opposed to something which is old; and often acceptance of the new is less dependent on either its intellectual force or its potential practical value than on the strength of the conventions and vested interest which sustains the old.

Some Major Organizational Changes in the Past Twenty-five Years

Little, if anything at all, has indeed changed over the years in the nature of the individual research worker. But when we compare the state of science today with what it was twenty-five years ago, several big changes stand out in the way we conduct our affairs. First, we are much more organized. Those of us who started our scientific careers before the Second World War can appreciate this fact only too readily. Second, much more research and development is now carried out by teams of research workers, sometimes big teams, rather than by individuals, than was ever the case before. Third, though we borrow each other's techniques, we have also tended to become more specialized, with an efflorescence of new journals. And, fourth, technological developments have not only made more science possible, but, on average, very much more expensive per research worker employed—particularly in the field of defense science. For example, there can be no area of science in which computers have not made it possible to undertake researches which could never have been dreamed of before. But, compared to the kind of equipment the scientist enjoyed in the thirties, computers cost big money. So do radio telescopes and particle accelerators and space vehicles.

An immediate consequence of all this is that however considerable, in terms of actual money, the resources that are now made available to scientists—pure and applied—their allocation calls increasingly for agreement about priorities. How is this to be done? Demands on the interests of scientists are fast outrunning their numbers. The interests of scientists are growing all the time. How can one conceive of a conscious balance of effort over the whole field of science when the latter is always changing, or, again, when so large an amount of the money that is made available for research and development comes from defense budgets, and when a great deal of the work which is carried out by scientists is shrouded in secrecy?

Priorities in Scientific Work

There has been much public debate about priorities in science these past few years, particularly these past three or four years, and a considerable intellectual effort has been made in different countries to agree on the principles which should dictate the proportion of public expenditure which should go, first, to the whole of research and development; second, to basic as opposed to "mission-orientated" or applied research—which some have aptly differentiated as curiosity-directed as opposed to need-directed research; and, third, to separate fields of science. We are still far from agreement on any of these matters. I myself am somewhat skeptical about our chances of ever finding a set of universal principles which will tell us how much support pure research should receive, whether we accept as a working assumption that the cultivation of basic science should be regarded as an "overhead" cost to the economic exploitation of scientific knowledge in general, whether it is something which should be supported as one of man's cultural activities, or whether the justification is a mixture of both these propositions.[4]

Priorities in Basic Research

The problem of priorities is, of course, not the same in the open world of basic research as it is in the more secret, even if wider, world in which applied science and development flourish. Some might suppose that because certain areas of basic science look as though they will pay off better and sooner than others, any good administrator could decide how much support to give different fields of basic science. That is not my view. I believe that scientists themselves can best decide how to allocate such resources for basic science as are provided from a total research-and-development budget. They may not do the job very well, but it is inconceivable that anyone else could do the job better, whatever the criteria by which the relative claims of different fields of work are judged, whether of possible utility or intellectual merit.

Nothing, as I have already implied, is static in science—neither fields of interest nor methods, techniques or what you will. Molecular biology began, as it were, yesterday; radio astronomy, which took off from radar, the day before that; as the involvement of European countries in overseas colonial territories declines, their interest in systematic helminthology and parasitology and tropical diseases declines; nuclear physics increased the number of atomic elements and radiochemistry revivified organic chemistry; lasers emerge and find a use in highly different fields ranging from tele-links in weapon systems to ophthalmic surgery. As the techniques of one branch of science become applied to another, new borderline subjects emerge, and these then become established as disciplines of their own. The changing pattern of science is thus not only like that of a turning kaleidoscope; it is that of a turning and expanding kaleidoscope, the beads and bits in which are added to hourly, and in an unpredictable way. As the pattern changes, so does the intellectual stimulus of its different parts. No one scientist understands the whole pattern, for in one sense all scientists are specialists. But in another we are all becoming borderline scientists. It is, therefore, a fair proposition that scientists as a class would be more likely than would nonscientists to get the sense of the whole changing pattern of science, and so to judge wisely about the value of new ideas and of work in progress. It is essentially for this reason that I hold that the main responsibility for deciding how to allocate the resources set aside for basic science should be firmly laid on representatives of the scientific community itself.

For all practical purposes, of course, these resources are totally deployed at any given moment, and proposals for change are automatically resisted. One reads about fixed research budgets being adjusted, and of dying points in research giving way to growing points, but one seldom hears about deliberate efforts to bring about the demise of a project once it has been started. The tendency is for a piece of research to go on till it dies a natural death because of intellectual, leading eventually to financial, inanition. Nonetheless, the new and inexpensive good research worker usually gets what he wants after the quality of his ideas and the excellence of his performance have been endorsed by the more experienced scientists who are usually called upon to act as judges by money-giving institutions. This happens even for scientists belonging to countries where very little money is spent on science, for if a man cannot get at home what he feels he needs in order to pursue his researches, he usually finds a way of obtaining it somewhere else—usually in the U.S.A.

The situation is very different when big money is wanted for some major new departure in basic science—say, for the provision of a new radio telescope or an accelerator. In these circumstances, the men who pronounce in the national interest on the quality and promise of scientific ideas have to agree among themselves that the resources which are being sought would be better spent on the new scheme than on some other expensive work to which they are already devoted and it is very difficult either to get agreement to such a decision or to implement it if it is agreed. There is always resistance to this kind of change. Basic scientists are usually specialists so far as field of interest is concerned, and redeployment, which would result from any such decision, does not always follow the rules of the marketplace.

Alternatively, the judges will have to agree that if new money can be raised, which is the usual way research budgets are adjusted, it would be better spent on the new scheme than on any of, say, a half-dozen other schemes in different areas of science which are also on the table awaiting decision. And someone else would have to agree that the new money could, in fact, be provided.

In the end the choice is largely determined by a combination of chance, advocacy and other intangibles. I should hardly imagine that any scientist would be prepared to argue that the present pattern of interests in basic science in different countries represents some rationally conceived and implemented plan. Working scientists might be more inclined to attribute the broad outlines of the pattern to the interaction of the inertia of past decision, and the play of present fashion.

Priorities in Applied Research and Development

When we come to some kinds of basic research which are mission-orientated and, more particularly, to applied research and then development, we are in an area of choice where the alternatives are, as a rule, both more expensive, and where judgment implies some prophetic view of the usefulness of the tangible things which may materialize from the work in the kind of world which will exist, say, ten years hence.

Many of us have experienced the unknowns in this kind of exercise, the doubts which balance conviction, and, when it comes to development work, the underestimation of difficulties. We know that the concept of utility is a relative one because the future usually turns out differently from what one imagined; and we also know that when it comes to utility, some line of approach to the same general end, and of which we might be unaware, may turn out to be far better than the one we have pursued.

In deciding the allocation of the large sums of public money which may be involved in all these more advanced stages of the scientific process, the voices of other judges—of politicians, administrators and industrialists—must be heard. But so, too, must that of the scientist, even if his views on the subject of utility may not be especially relevant. For although he may be as impotent as his nonscientific colleagues in predicting the social consequences of scientific discovery, the scientist knows better than they what the technical facts are, and about the possibility of their successful exploitation.

The Maintenance of Standards

When scientists are called in to play a part in the determination of priorities, more is called for than just the qualities that make them good scientists in the laboratory or the field. But since these qualities are basic to the rest, let us first remind ourselves of what they are—in the ideal.

First and foremost a scientist must be a man who adheres strictly to the rules of scientific method; a realization that experiments and observations have to be properly controlled must be part of his second nature. Obviously he should also have an intimate and wide knowledge of his field of specialization. He should be endowed with creative imagination, judgment and technical skill, as well as with persistence and a proclivity for hard work. His capacity for honest self-criticism should be highly developed and combined with an ability to take criticism from others. He should also be open-minded to the fact that progress, technical or otherwise, in one field may affect progress or direction in another. I could add other qualities, but these are enough to go on with in painting the outlines of a scientific paragon.

Scientists vary enormously both in the extent to which they embody these virtues and in their general abilities. Partly as a result, the scientific process has itself generated a unique set of devices for assuring the high quality of scientific work. The first is the fact that scientists, whenever they possibly can, publish the results of their researches. If a particular piece of scientific work is no good, it will, either immediately or in time, be exposed as such; and a scientist who becomes known for bad work is soon finished. The second is the existence of national academies of science with limited memberships restricted to the best men. To the layman, and to scientists as well, these academies are the embodiment of the prestige of science and, as a result, become the most important guardians of quality. The third is the existence of international institutions which accord rewards for scientific work of the highest quality, such, for example, as the Nobel prizes.

So far I have spoken only about the qualities which one would expect to find in the ideal scientist, and about the mechanisms whereby the world of science assures its own standards of excellence. To them must be added more general virtues when we seek for people who would be competent to advise on science policy, by which I essentially mean advise about the most reasonable ways in which the scientific resources of a country can be cultivated and deployed. First of all, we would seek not just narrow specialists, but men who have some idea of what goes on in fields of science other than their own, and who have the competence and interest to learn. Second, we would seek people with the minimum of prejudice—certainly about subjects if not about persons. And finally—and this perhaps is the most difficult—we would seek men whose sophistication extended outside the domains of science, men who have an awareness of the vast changes which are taking place in the world as a whole, and of the forces which are bringing them about.

But having drawn my blueprint, I have to ask whether it is a realistic one. Is the environment of today one which provides the best conditions either for the emergence of the scientific ideal or for scientific progress? My own answer would be, I fear, very equivocal. While the material opportunities for scientists have never been better, there are many dangers in the present situation. The scientific world is being subdivided not only by its multifarious interests, but also by the facts of international and national secrecy, commercial as well as military. Those who are responsible to their peers for advising on national science policies are in serious difficulty because of these secret worlds of science. So, too, are individual scientific workers. Equally, the vast resources which have been made available for scientific work have created what some have called a scientific rat race, and have also made it possible for some kinds of pseudoscience to emerge and to confuse the scene, particularly in areas of defense science. Let me deal separately with these issues.

Secrecy

The open world of science is mainly concerned with the secrets of nature which are laid bare by the researcher. In the closed world of science are the secrets of the researcher which have to be guarded because of national or commercial considerations. No active defense scientist, nor any academic scientist who may at some time or other have been engaged in government work, would question the proposition that certain kinds of information must be protected in the interests of national security. This kind of secrecy is necessary, often vital; but in a very real sense it is also something which is bad for science.

That is so because communication is a necessary part of the scientific process. Work which is done in secret almost always suffers in quality because it is not exposed to the full blaze of scientific criticism. Secrecy also means that the main body of science is always in danger of being kept in ignorance, at least for a time, of some germinal idea or some new and far-reaching technique. In addition, secrecy in government laboratories may hinder the economic exploitation of new discoveries, and lead to the pursuit in parallel, and in partial if not complete ignorance, of fields of study which necessitate highly expensive facilities. The question which we need to ask, therefore, is whether the considerations which argue for secrecy always outweigh its deleterious effects, and how the latter can be mitigated. We first need to ask what it is that we gain by secrecy, even in the defense field.

In the days before scientific journals began to appear—in the latter half of the seventeenth century—the small number of scientists who were alive at any one time kept each other informed, by way of direct correspondence, about the work they were doing. Journals provided an easier and wider method of communication, and also eventually a means whereby the individual scientist could satisfy his desire to proclaim his discoveries to the world, in an effort to "get in first." The fear that one's incipient discoveries might be preempted from some unknown quarter is both an urge to secrecy when a piece of work is in progress, and a spur to publication when it is completed. But in spite of the understandable impulse which may lead a scientist to suppress information about some brainchild of his until he feels the time is ripe to disclose it, I do not think that secrecy plays any useful part in the open world of science. Indeed, I should be inclined to say that the temptation to succumb to the impulse would normally be in inverse proportion to the quality of the work, and to the quality of the man concerned.

We are no longer in the days of, say, Lavoisier, when, because of the small numbers of scientists in the world, it might have been expected that discoveries would usually be the product of only one mind, and that they would emerge at one particular moment in time. Scientists, who were once numbered in their tens, are now counted in thousands and tens of thousands. We all base ourselves on a common pool of knowledge. We all know the general form of the "hot problems" in physics, or chemistry, or genetics. When we exclude the small number of absolutely novel discoveries or hypotheses which constitute the foundation stones of the body of scientific knowledge, and which are added to only rarely, we need not feel surprised if in these days the same ideas are formulated more than once, in different parts of the world, and often about the same time. It is almost inconceivable that a Mendel could today report the basic law of genetics and that no one would pick it up till thirty years later. What is more likely is that we would find that more than one Mendel had been thinking along the same lines, that two, three, or four of them were about to publish their results at about the same time—and much the same results. In the pursuit and exploitation of new concepts we almost always seem to find several laboratories pursuing similar courses. We can recall only too well how much parallel development of the same projects occurred in England and America on the one hand, and Germany on the other, during the course of the Second World War.

Secrecy, of course, plays a powerful role in the commercial

world. It is indeed difficult to conceive of an industrial undertaking which diverts its own resources to research, revealing to its competitors knowledge which it may have gained at great expense. But the question is to what extent should commercial scientific secrecy be taken? I would not go so far as some who declare that it would pay to publish everything, in the hopes that doing so would be more likely to confuse than benefit a rival firm, which would otherwise be focusing its intelligence efforts in trying to find out what really mattered. But I have a feeling that a contrary policy of publishing little or nothing probably goes too far. In any event, there are considerations more important than secrecy which affect the assessment of the commercial value of the results of industrial research and development.

To what extent is it wise to carry secrecy in the basic researches which we pursue in our government laboratories, whether their motivation is "pure" or "mission-orientated"? A further question that we need to ask is who should decide—the scientists or an independent body of security officials? What, to put a third question, does the "need-to-know" rule of security mean in fields of basic science—I am, of course, excluding from consideration the need for security when we talk of development for clearly defined weapon systems. Here there can be no question: security is an essential rule.

To try and illustrate the problem, let us turn to one of the best technical secrets of all time, the work which led during the course of the Second World War to the development of the nuclear bomb. At its start it was hardly a secret at all. It was certainly not a military secret. The scientists in whose minds the idea was born themselves decided, as a corporate voluntary act, to curtail open publication of any information which might point in the direction of a bomb. When the idea of a nuclear weapon became an officially defined project, government administrators, in both the U.K. and the U.S., found themselves in a quandary because of the number of refugee scientists who were involved. But in spite of the administrators' opposition—I quote from the official British history[5] of the subject—"the greatest of all the wartime secrets was entrusted to scientists excluded for security reasons from other war work." Later, officials in our two countries argued about the manner and extent to which security should be maintained, and at the end of the war the British authorities expressed strong opposition, on grounds of security, to the publication by Dr. Smyth of his famous report on the Manhattan Project, a volume which the U.S. authorities felt needed to appear in print. Here the British authorities concerned were almost certainly too cautious. Niels Bohr, whose intervention in the politics of nuclear affairs had a better reception at the hands of President Roosevelt than at those of Mr. Churchill, as well as Sir James Chadwick, one of the most distinguished of the British contributors to the project, believed that the mechanics of the bomb could not be held secret for long, and for this reason they argued for the international control of the atom well before the end of the Second World War. What happened? Even though every effort was made to prevent information passing to other governments about the design and construction of bombs, and the construction and operation of plants producing fissile material, other governments —and not just the U.S.S.R.—did find out. And many who have not yet revealed a knowledge of the subject probably know its secrets, which no doubt they would already have put to use had they judged it in their political interest to do so, and had they had the resources, scientific and financial, which the enterprise would have demanded.

What, then, did we gain by the imposition of secrecy? The main prize was obviously time. And essentially this is probably all that security ever gains in any scientific field. In the end, in most cases sooner rather than later, we can expect other people, our opponents or competitors, to discover what we know. The purpose of security in the technical field is to prolong the time it takes them to learn, and so to add to their costs. In the case of the bomb the prize was at first priceless. It has been argued by some that the additional military security which we can attribute to the nuclear secrecy of more recent years has been all but counterbalanced by certain political problems which it has also generated.

In the light of this story I turn back to my three questions. How far should we keep the basic researches we do in government laboratories secret; who should decide; and what does the "need-to-know" principle of security mean in this area of science?

The answer to all these questions is, to my mind, pointed by the fact that the most potent knowledge which ever emerges from the pursuit of basic science can never be recognized as such, and consequently that it can never be guarded at its birth. In spite of the fabulous influence it was to have on military and political affairs, could anyone today conceive in retrospect of any reason why news of Einstein's work should have been suppressed when it first emerged? Why was the enormous importance of D.D.T. on the one hand, and antibiotic action on the other, not recognized at the start? If it had been, would some pharmaceutical house have been justified in suppressing the information? What conceivable good could have resulted from any efforts to suppress the basic work which led up to radar—at a time when its practical significance was, in fact, not recognized?

Another consideration which affects my own answer to these questions of security in basic science, whether pure or "mission-orientated," is that I do not believe that the source of the great ideas which have transformed the scientific scene has ever been the secret laboratories of governments. It is in the open world, not the closed world of military science, where the big ideas have germinated, sprouted and flowered. This is not because the inherent creative quality of the men who have worked in government laboratories was or is on average below what one finds in, say, a university department. Far from it. My hunch is that the young man who starts working under conditions of secrecy in a field which is defined for him by his superiors is less likely to enjoy the riches of imaginative discovery than the man working in a free and open environment where his work is exposed to the full blaze of scientific criticism. Secrecy and great thoughts do not thrive together.

The third point which determines my judgment in this matter is the fact that the vast growth in scientific activity of the past two to three decades has paradoxically made it difficult for anyone to keep up with what is published, even in the open world of science. We are involved in what has been called a "crisis in communication." So much is published that, secrecy or no secrecy, the average scientist is likely to be ignorant of published observations which could help galvanize his own work. Whatever else, he does not want to do work which has been done already. When one adds to this the fact that the research worker often fails to realize the significance of one or some of his own observations—we all have had experience of this—it becomes all the more important that there should be no unnecessary barriers to information which someone else can provide. A trivial thought, captured from anywhere, from some printed sentence, from the storehouse of memory, can suddenly illuminate what has been obscure, and by so doing bring about a revolution in understanding.

It is all very well hoping that some modern computer system by which the mounting flood of new scientific information is codified, processed and reassembled as required is going to get us over the difficulty of communication. Whatever can be done by modern bibliographical methods to draw a scientist's attention to a piece of information which might be critical to his work—and a lot can be done—we have to recognize, as Fox[6] so rightly says, that "machines cannot distinguish good papers from bad ones . . . nor can they answer those often crucial questions . . . the ones the enquirer does not know how to ask."

In order to clear channels of communication in the open world of science, we have had to return in recent years to the direct exchange of information between small groups of people working in the same field, people who correspond with each other, and meet repeatedly at national and international symposia. I share the hope that these and other devices will improve the situation. But the chances would be all the better if men who work in basic areas of science, whether or not they relate directly or indirectly to technical problems of national defense, were not unnecessarily impeded in exchanging their scientific knowledge with others.

It seems ridiculous that there can be people working on the same problems of basic science who, for reasons of presumed security, are unaware of each other's existence, and certainly unaware of each other's results. But this, I am sure, is the case for scientists within the United Kingdom and the United States of America. We know the need for security when it comes to project work—but this is not what I am writing about. The issue is basic science, whether it is "curiosity" or "need-orientated." And to go back to my earlier point—how on earth can those who are responsible for advising about the proper allocation of a country's scientific resources to basic science contribute of their best when they may be unaware of what is happening behind their own country's security curtains, where a significant proportion of the work is done. It is bad enough that they are sometimes unaware of what is going on in the open!

There are enough barriers already in the open world of science leading to the separation of individual research workers not to erect others which may not be necessary. All in all, and on the basis of my own experience, I should, therefore, conclude that more is lost by throwing security cloaks over the kind of basic science which is done in government laboratories than is ever to be gained. What is more, I do not believe that anyone has sufficient knowledge and skill to take upon himself the responsibility for imposing any "need-to-know" security principles in these areas of science.

Secrecy prevents free critical discussion and, as I have said, so conduces to a decline in quality. If basic science must be pursued in government laboratories, even in government laboratories which are also concerned with applied and development work, leading, say, to weapon systems, I would, therefore, argue that wherever possible, arrangements should be made for it to become part of the open world of science. This is the policy which we are trying to implement in the United Kingdom, in the full recognition that occasionally there may be difficulties in differentiating certain kinds of applied science from what is basic. Were this policy to be effective, the men concerned would not only be better able to judge the quality and necessity of their own studies; they would also stand a better chance of gaining prestige and stature in the world of science as a whole, instead of living apart as isolated members. It might be that exceptions should on occasion have to be made to the conclusion I am putting forward; but I must confess that possible ones relating to basic science which have flitted through my mind do not encourage me to weaken my proposition. The thought keeps returning that the same characteristics of unpredictability and the same methods of inquiry apply to basic research whether it is "pure" in the sense that it does not relate as yet to some known field of exploitation, or if it is being pursued in a field where the possibilities of practical exploitation are already recognized. The danger that a piece of work, if published, might give a clue to the applied interests of the establishment in which it is being carried out could, I feel, be mitigated by administrative procedures. The essential point about the publication of the results of truly basic research is that the research worker himself should always be conscious of the right to publish—unless good reason is shown why he should not.

There is an additional point. In the world of military science secrecy does not, as we are only too well aware, inevitably prevent treachery, any more than treachery has been completely eliminated from other parts of the military machine. If it had been, what need would there be for parts of the secret services we maintain?

Science, Pseudoscience and Value Judgments

The basic science about which I am writing is the body of knowledge which has been rigorously established through the use

of genuine methods of scientific inquiry. I am talking particularly about what can still be called the "natural sciences." As
scientists, we know what they are, and we know how they have
been built up with the years. We also know how new "sciences"
are born. If it were ever to become the case that the "occult
sciences" became scientific, or that water-divining became a
science, they would do so only because scientific methods of
inquiry had made them so. Primitive man found his minerals by
following outcrops of rock back into the earth, having first
learned that some other material, a metal—gold, copper, or
tin—for which he had found a use, could be extracted from the
rock by smelting. He learned to recognize the rocks he wanted
by particular characteristics which he could discern by eye.
Today the geologist uses not only the eyes with which he is born,
but also new eyes that have been furnished through the advances
of science—magnetometers, Geiger counters, boring equipment
and so on. He uses scientific methods of observation and analysis
to build a corpus of knowledge which not only "explains" the
past and present, but also foretells part of the future. That is the
only way a science can be created, the only way areas of human
interest ever become transformed into bodies of knowledge con-
sisting of propositions which have the dual characteristics of
effective stability and predictive value.

Secrecy cannot but distort this kind of orderly growth. So, too,
does the confusion about science which is only too often conjured up in the lay mind during these days of rapid scientific
development. With so much science in the air, areas of interest
or discussion become treated as scientific whether or not they are
subject to the real discipline of scientific method. We live in an
age of more and more science, and also, alas, more pseudoscience. This, as I suggested earlier, is one of the unfortunate
facts of our time. It, too, certainly does not help provide the best
conditions for scientific progress. The public is led to believe
that anything is science if it has numbers in it, or demands slide
rules, or is carried out by people with a Ph.D.

There is a border zone of interest where the issues with which we deal in defense science start incorporating value judgments, such as the concept of effectiveness, leading on to cost effectiveness. This is a kind of gray zone between genuine science and pseudoscience. Within it I would also include some kinds of operational analysis and systems analysis with which the defense scientist has become fairly familiar, and to which I have referred in my opening chapter. In my own view, some kinds of systems analysis begin to verge on the scientific. Others do not and never will, even though their object is to make precise and to translate into numerical language the issues on which major decisions need to be taken. They cannot become truly scientific because when one course of action is chosen and others rejected as a result of a piece of systems analysis, the situation becomes totally transformed. The implementation of the choice makes it impossible to return to the subject to test the situation afresh— which it is always possible to do in a true science.

This is a major difference. Science, as I said, is more than just numbers, and more than slide rules. It is more than just objective or dispassionate analysis. When scientific inquiry steps out of its own ground and treads into the area of value judgments, it starts to become something more than science, and something which then begins to partake of the controversial character of economics, or even of politics.

Tradition has it that economists can never agree among themselves when it comes to debate about economic policy, whereas scientists, as scientists, always tend to agree about methods of analysis and about the solutions to their problems. The reasons for the difficulties which face the economist are, according to a recent article by Fritz Machlup,[7] fourfold. First, economists are straightaway confronted by differences in semantics. The established rules of scientific method are there to help the scientist over that obstacle. Second, economists are apt to differ from each other in logical approach. Here again the scientist ought to be protected by the rules of the game. Third, economists are very prone to differ in their factual assumptions. Once more the advantage is to the scientist. And finally, economists differ because of differing value judgments associated with the aims of different courses of action.

I live in the hope that these differences between the social and the exact sciences are merely a reflection of the fact that the latter are further advanced in their formal evolution than is, say, the subject of economics. There is probably no logical reason why, in time, economists should not be provided with the basic scientific framework and apparatus of working which will be able to impose the necessary discipline on subjective and wishful thoughts, as is now possible within the body of science.

But at the moment it remains true that it is only when we come to value judgments that in theory the scientist is exposed to the same blaze of difficulties as the economist, with the added disadvantage that because the scientist is always expected to agree with the body of scientific fact, it is also expected that there will be a single scientific point of view on matters which are external to the facts themselves. This disadvantage is a real one, simply because the occurrence of such disagreements tends sometimes to discredit what is thought of as *the* scientific point of view on matters of policy, scientific and otherwise. On the other hand, because scientists normally operate in conditions which do not permit of arbitrary disagreement, they are probably better able than others to appreciate the factors which lead to disagreement, when disagreement occurs. And they are better able, at all times, to tell the difference between science and pseudoscience—that at least they should be.

Conclusion

Value judgments are the final determinants of priorities in the allocation of resources in the world of science. In the fields of basic science the judgments relate to the quality of ideas and the excellence of observation. Here the scientist is on his own. When we come to applied research, and particularly to development, the scientist is joined by others who help call the tune. In the applications of science the big issues are in the end political

—military security, health, welfare and so on. The scientist, as I have insisted, has a part to play in the choice, in the same way as he appreciates better than anyone else that there can be no secrets in basic science—and few indeed in applied science. As Wiesner[8] has put it, "an advancing technology and an uncertain world call for an extraordinary effort to encompass technical considerations with which the majority of the people are largely unfamiliar." This, if anything, is clearly a central job for the scientist. The less secrecy, the greater the exchange of information, the more open the world of science, the better will the scientist be able to discharge his responsibilities, not only in the laboratory but also in the arena where policy is made—however much his technical considerations have to be qualified by value judgments.

PART II

Science and Society

6

Liberty in the Age of Science*

I FORGET WHO FIRST INTRODUCED ME TO THE WRITINGS OF George Gissing,[1] nor can I recall when my attention was drawn to that eloquent passage in *The Private Papers of Henry Ryecroft* in which Gissing (alias Ryecroft) proclaims against the dangers of science:

I wonder [he asked] whether there are many men who have the same feeling with regard to "science" as I have? It is something more than a prejudice; often it takes the form of a dread, almost a terror. Even those branches of science which are concerned with things that interest me—which deal with plants and animals and the heaven of stars—even these I cannot contemplate without uneasiness, a spiritual disaffection; new discoveries, new theories, however they engage my intelligence, soon weary me, and in some way depress. When it comes to other kinds of science—the sciences blatant and ubiquitous—the science by which men become millionaires—I am possessed with an angry hostility, a resentful apprehension. . . .

I hate and fear "science" [he went on] because of my conviction that, for long to come if not forever, it will be the remorseless enemy of mankind. I see it destroying all simplicity and gentleness of life, all the beauty of the world; I see it restoring barbarism under a mask of civilization; I see it darkening men's minds and hardening their hearts; I see it bringing a time of vast conflicts, which will pale into insignificance "the thousand wars of old," and, as likely as not, will

* The text of the main part of the Commencement Address delivered at the California Institute of Technology on June 12, 1959.

125

whelm all the laborious advances of mankind in blood-drenched chaos.

Gissing lived long before the age of artificial satellites, and long before the era of nuclear weapons. The disquiet he felt, even in the relatively calm technological days of the turn of the nineteenth century, is as easy to understand as is that which has been expressed in more recent years by equally articulate voices. In a vivid passage A. J. P. Taylor[2] has declaimed against scientists to whom "any argument will do" so long as they "can go on with their terribly sweet problems"—quoting a phrase used by Dr. Robert Oppenheimer, the first leader of the U.S. atomic energy program, in the Congressional hearings which brought his Washington career to an end. "The scientists think they are God," Taylor goes on, "they want to remake the universe; and we pay the price for their mad ambition. . . . Shall we," he asks, "knock the power out of their hands before it is too late?" J. B. Priestley[3] talks of our social irresponsibility, of our fanaticism, and asks whether, like politicians, we have not "now been given too much power without being qualified to use it properly." And I believe that it was James Thurber who wrote: "Man is flying too fast for a world that is round. Soon he will catch up with himself in a great rear-end collision and Man will never know that what hit him from behind was Man."

Eloquent and appealing though all this may be, the underlying thought, nonetheless, reveals both a deep misunderstanding of what science is, and a dangerous confusion between the concept of scientific knowledge and the uses to which it has always been put in satisfying human demands and needs.

Private and Public Science

Science is no more than the body of "exact" knowledge which is always being added to by scientists, through controlled and reproducible observations. Its furtherance constitutes an endeavor which is either personal and private, or social and public. But however pure or personal may be the object of acquiring a scientific understanding of some aspect of the universe in which we have our being, science inevitably becomes social or public not only because there can be no awareness of the existence of a new scientific idea until it is communicated from one person to another, but also because pure science frequently turns out to be basic to some practical development—to some piece of applied science—or to some convention of thought, which then starts transforming the environment within which it was distilled. So it is that pure science and applied science have progressed hand in hand over the years, the pure fertilizing the applied with ideas, and the applied often providing the pure with the physical apparatus to help in the next intellectual leap forward.

This process has been a major factor in the progressive replacement of superstition by rational theory. As Condorcet[4]— the great French mathematician of the latter half of the eighteenth century, and the revolutionary who was so powerful a champion of human dignity and freedom—wrote: "The progress of the sciences ensures the progress of the art of education which in turn advances that of the sciences"—a reciprocal operation which he did not exaggerate by describing it "as one of the most powerful and active causes working for the perfection of mankind."

This process has also meant the continuous transformation of our social institutions through the directed application of pure scientific knowledge. We talk today of living in a new age of science, of a world in the throes of a new scientific revolution: but there is nothing new about this revolution except its speed and its greater hazards. Science and the applications of science have always revolutionized society, ever since some basic discoveries in animal husbandry and crop cultivation made it possible for nomadic life to give way—ten to twenty thousand years ago—to permanent village settlements, and so to the diversification of labor and the beginning of trade.

The transformation of society by scientific discovery and application has continued ever since, sometimes so slowly that decades pass before the historical record reveals much change;

sometimes, as at present, with violent force and far-reaching consequence. It is widely held, for example, that the introduction of gunpowder into Europe, and the subsequent development of cannon and other firearms, were ultimately responsible for the transference of the sovereign power of the medieval state from feudal barons and monarchs to the people over whom they had previously held sway. Later, in the early eighteenth century, the determined development of steam power in order to make machines which could be used in mining and manufacturing brought about an industrial revolution whose repercussions on the social and political organization of the world were probably even more profound than the original agrarian revolution—if we can call it that—which made village life possible in the mesolithic and neolithic eras.

It can, of course, be argued that the technical advances of the past ten to twenty years transcend those of the rest of human history; that the speed with which new discoveries are disseminated and applied is now unprecedented; that the political and economic consequences of all this scientific activity will prove far more profound than those which resulted from past epochs of discovery. But, nonetheless, there is no immediate reason to suppose that the social process which is involved in today's scientific revolution is different in kind from what was entailed in previous phases of rapid change.

If we are to understand the confused position in which the layman and the scientist now stand in relation to each other, we need therefore to examine certain features which characterize the growth of scientific knowledge, and also some which relate to its present impact on social affairs. And since the theme of this chapter is liberty in an age of science, let us first consider the concept of academic freedom as it applies to the pure scientist.

The Uniqueness of Discovery

As I understand it, the term means not only the freedom to investigate those problems which one seeks oneself, but also the fact that significant advances in scientific knowledge cannot be ordered by decree. Every act of creation requires its special freedom. For example, it may well be—as some now suggest—that the idea of antibiotic action may have been immanent in certain primitive and ancient household remedies. But before Fleming, Florey and Chain discovered penicillin, and before scientific experiment made it possible to formulate a general concept of antibiotic action, there was nothing to discuss, and no point of departure in a search for other antibiotics.

This applies, too, to vitamins. Today we are told that the Eskimos have known for generations about the health-giving virtues of minute quantities of certain fatty foods, and that the Afghans have long had "vitamin" pills made from caviar. But the concept of accessory food factors and vitamins was lacking, and it could not be used to galvanize man's thoughts, till it was given life by men like Funk and Gowland Hopkins.

The same is true of every other basic idea of science. Our theories of thermodynamics, of relativity, of natural selection, of genetics, undoubtedly had their antecedent relations. "What happens at any particular moment is the result of what has happened at all previous moments, and itself has an influence on what will happen in the future." Condorcet, who wrote this nearly two hundred years ago, was not the first to express this thought; and I shall certainly not be the last to repeat it. Every great scientific discovery clearly emerges from its relevant matrix. But no one could have predicted, before it actually occurred, if, and how, and when any of these major advances in our scientific understanding would take place. Nor would it be possible to force a scientist to make this or that specified discovery. For example, genius though he was, no one could have prevailed upon Charles Darwin, say, in 1830, when he was twenty years old, to anticipate the basic genetic law revealed by Gregor Mendel thirty-five years later. One can employ special measures to encourage this or that branch of science. One can provide the conditions in which pure science flourishes, by multiplying the opportunities which make it possible—the universities, the laboratories, the freedom from other responsibilities. But having done these things, one can only then wait to see what emerges. One cannot in advance specify the shape and content, or determine the possible impact of what is not yet known.

Being unpredictable, it follows that the untrammeled emergence of new scientific ideas is not compatible with any restraint on the liberty of the scientist to roam where his fancy leads. Indeed, once the growth of any set of scientific ideas becomes constrained, it stands in danger of becoming obstructive dogma. A valid scientific hypothesis is never more than the best statement which, for the moment, can be made of the relations of the matters to which it refers, and should be swept away as soon as a better one emerges.

Science, which is based upon our most rational processes of thought, and which is dependent on reproducible experiment, is inevitably revolutionary in its methods. And it is revolutionary in a very special way. No moral obligation rests upon the scientist to set up a new hypothesis to replace another which his observations may have invalidated. Naturally one would prefer it if he did. But he would still deserve our gratitude if he destroyed some false belief and by so doing, saved us from its continuing tyranny, even if his competence for the moment was unequal to the task of indicating where a more adequate understanding lay.

The growth of science thus necessitates absolute freedom, even the freedom to be revolutionary. One might well ask, therefore, whether stability can ever be achieved in a world in which science has so great an impact. How does science become, as it was described by a recent President of the United States[5]— "the servant and the handmaiden" of the freedom which is the central ideal of Western democracy?

Science the Servant of Society

It seems clear that what he had in mind was the simple proposition that since economic and military power are today in part a function of the degree to which scientific knowledge is exploited, science is the defender of the ideal of freedom on which Western democracy rests. In a more particular sense, as many have pointed out before, the applications of science have also provided the apparatus which has made central government powerful.

But science is in these respects no more the servant of the democracies than of the authoritarian regimes poised against them, and of the philosophical and political concepts on which they, in turn, are based. Our world is divided into a large number of separate national entities, each of which enjoys, through the sanction of international law, sovereign power within its separate area. Some regulate their affairs, to greater or lesser extent, according to the basic concepts of Western democracy—of which in practice the most important is government by consent. Others, in varying degree, are authoritarian regimes. In both categories we find nations which are rich, nations which are poor; nations which already enjoy the fruits of highly developed industrial economies, and nations whose economies are under-developed; nations which are favored by sophisticated educational systems, and nations which are in large part illiterate. Everywhere—both in our own democratic and in the authoritarian worlds—we find the same urge for greater personal fulfillment, for higher standards of living, for more speedy economic advancement, coupled only too often with an overriding frustration, which at the national level translates itself into a sense of insecurity deriving from the clash of conflicting interests in the international arena. What we have to realize, therefore, is that in a world of conflicting power, science is both the arsenal and the instrument of power—but that science *qua* science is always a neutral arsenal and a neutral instrument.

We cannot invest pure scientific knowledge with any inherent moral direction. That is imparted by the way science is used. All we can be certain of is that all sides in the present world struggle will use science and technology where and how they can in the achievement of their respective national aims; and also in whatever efforts they may make to narrow the ever-widening gap between the developed and underdeveloped territories of the world.

My first main point, therefore, is that while the growth of fundamental scientific knowledge necessitates complete freedom from restraint, science is not uniquely associated with the preservation of freedom in either the personal or the social sphere.

Science and the Concept of Liberty

But there is a deeper issue underlying the relation of science and freedom. Let me first define the sense in which I propose talking about the concept of freedom or liberty, which, both in isolation and as the ideal which animates democracy, has always been a major concern of philosophical discussion.

By freedom I understand the liberty an individual enjoys after the infinite number of degrees of freedom which are open to him in the abstract have been reduced by the give-and-take of social life, still leaving a vast area of choice within which he could either engage in, or desist from, any particular activity. It was essentially in this sense that the great utilitarians of the industrial revolution—Bentham, John Stuart Mill and others who joined them in the battle for justice—conceived of freedom in the ideal society: a society which is governed by common consent for the common good; in which the greatest number enjoy the greatest happiness; in which there is equality of suffrage, and, in theory at least, of educational and economic opportunity; and in which laws and institutions, regulating the behavior of individuals, are there because the unlimited exercise of one man's liberty would inevitably impose restrictions on that of his fellows. "No one can remain absolutely free; we must give up some liberty to preserve the rest."[6]

It is essentially in this social sense, however "negative" it may be, to use Berlin's term, that liberty is implied in the proposition that science is its handmaiden. Science may well be the handmaiden of equality in the economic sphere, given, of course, the right kind of political institutions. This has long been one of man's enduring hopes. As Saint-Simon[7] wrote: "the domination of the physical environment by science and industry will progressively emancipate man, not merely from want and insecurity, but also from the domination of some men by others." But is the proposition true that science is the handmaiden of liberty in the philosophical sense of the term "liberty," whether in relation to the concept to which I am directing my observations or to any other ideas of liberty which philosophers have examined? Can the proposition that science is the handmaiden of liberty be true of the actual environment within which we exercise our freedom—an environment which is not some unreal stratosphere peopled either by philosophers or by abstract shadows of human beings or of social groups? Surely our social environment is a real one which is constantly being transformed by new scientific ideas, and by the application and practical development of these ideas. This transformation constitutes more than a process whereby men are conditioned in their thoughts and actions. Whenever some major development is pursued—for example, the development of machines based on steam—it means that some other path that potentially might have been followed was not followed. A material civilization of motorcars, of radio, of synthetic fibers, of nuclear power is not necessarily the only form a material civilization might have taken. But now that it has taken that shape, it helps define for us the content and boundaries of the area within which we exercise our freedom.

Liberty, in the sense I am using the term (a sense used by most political philosophers), means the power to act freely within the compass of the institutions which a people may set up in the exercise of their sovereign power, which implies their right to act as they think best as a collective body and which, according to legal theory, "is not constrained in any way except by the limitations inherent in human nature." It is irrelevant here that the exercise of democracy may not infrequently depart from its ideals; or that the institutions which had to be set up to preserve the hard-won freedom of modern times may themselves have eroded the principles they were meant to preserve. The point I wish to make is that science, through its practical impact, is to an increasing extent, almost to a dominant extent, determining the way the presumedly uninhibited sovereign power expresses itself. Because of its achievements in eliminating disease and alleviating pain, through the food and wealth it has brought, most people today prefer to regulate their lives in accordance with scientific discovery and the exploitation of scientific discovery rather than in any other way. In that sense they are prepared to constrain their abstract liberties in accordance with what science unfolds, and the riches it brings. Is the choice, we may ask, conscious? Can we know what it is for which we are opting? Hobbes, like other philosophers, found liberty consistent with necessity. Is liberty truly consistent with necessity, when necessity is determined by science? Is the sovereign power consciously deciding to develop this or that scientific discovery, and so to determine social development in this or that direction? Or is it merely adapting itself as best it can to what falls out of the cornucopia of science?

The Unpredictable Consequences of Science

The answer to any of these questions is inevitably bound up with both the constraints and the unpredictability of any new major scientific advance. Of course, there are always certain fields of science which are more popular and better supported than others. Scientific knowledge never develops evenly over the whole potential field of knowledge. But insofar as scientific activity is in general confined by past discovery to certain areas, so is our abstract liberty, in effect, constrained. Furthermore, in any field of science, several alternative courses of action might be pursued in search for a solution to a problem. In choosing any one of them, the research worker may deny himself, and others, the opportunity of pursuing another. There is also the increasing complexity of the scientific knowledge which is now being transformed into new remedies, new chemicals, weapon systems and so on. The facts which these days transform our lives become more and more difficult to comprehend, and on occasion are still not fully decided when they are applied. If this were not so, would there still be debate—I choose the most urgent example of all—about the hazards associated with radioactive fallout?[8]

Above all is the fact that the nature and magnitude of potential discovery cannot be defined in advance; any more than can its impact on our social lives. As de Tocqueville[9] wrote: "We entrust ourselves to the future, an enlightened and impartial judge—but one who sits, alas, always too late."

Faraday, Hertz, Curie—what could they have known of the ultimate uses to which their discoveries would be put in the field of electric power, radio and nuclear energy; or of the social and political consequences of their uses. What ideas did Stephenson, Watt, Boulton or other great figures of the industrial revolution of the eighteenth century have of the vast social and economic consequences of their technological inventions? We ourselves, years later, cannot tell what these consequences will be. Can we, to refer to just one more vital question out of many new ones this scientific age is generating, commit ourselves now to more than arbitrary views of the possible political consequences of the elimination of disease and of its complementary change, the explosive growth of population in so many areas of the globe?

Science has created wealth; it has helped in the struggle for freedom from economic exploitation; it has redistributed power. But in doing these things, as it widens the area of material choice, it circumscribes and determines the environment in which we live and in which we exercise our abstract liberties. That is my second point. Itself demanding freedom, and revolutionary in its way, science is now determining, in an increasingly unpredictable way, the main issues about which we, as citizens, exercise our freedom of choice. Can there be much more than a fictional verity to the abstract idea that an area exists within which men can enjoy the capacity of unconditioned or untrammeled choice? How, in the preservation of personal freedom—I quote Berlin[6]—can a frontier be drawn between the area of private life and that of public authority if, as I have argued, the content of our material and intellectual environment is constantly changed, and in unpredictable ways, by the results of scientific inquiry?

Democracy was man's answer to tyranny and exploitation. The only form of exploitation it will never help overcome is the coercion of new knowledge, which, by guiding our social lives into certain channels, limits advance in other directions; the new knowledge which focuses the interests of humanity on goals which cannot be properly charted until they have been achieved. To the philosopher, as I have said, ultimate limitations on the freedom of the individual are set by the inexorable laws of Nature. To the scientist, the limitations are set by the particular laws of Nature man himself discovers, out of a potential infinity of such laws, and from the use to which he puts these laws.

Up to now we have been able to claim that the applications of science have increased the sum total of human happiness. But today we stand at a crossroad. The process of applying scientific knowledge is as endless as is the prospect of gathering new knowledge, and the basic scientist is responsible for only the beginning of the cycle of activity which creates a demand for the application of his discoveries. Industrialization has established itself as the one sure cure for poverty in a world the bulk of whose population still lives by subsistence farming; and history as yet gives no example of any but small communities which have voluntarily turned their backs on higher material standards of living. Instead, a uniformity of desire and demand is generated for the so-called good things of life as the one world discovers how the other lives, and what it itself lacks. Obviously we cannot say that the economic history of the West will be recapitulated as industrialization spreads, and as the chains of the past are broken in distant parts of the world. But we can be all but certain that neither the needy nor the rich will allow the process of applying the fruits of scientific knowledge to stop, either in the national or in the international frame. In this process means become ends, because as new ways of doing things are discovered, they transform the things being done, and so their purpose. In these days it is only in theory that one chooses weapons and tactics to achieve a strategy. In fact, weapons often end by determining strategy—and sometimes the purpose behind the strategy.

In my view it is against this force of scientific application that the Gissings of today rail—not against science as such; and it is this force which could constrain our democratic liberties, and which, if we ceased being vigilant, could even constrain the liberty of pure and basic science—and by so doing paradoxically destroy itself.

We need to remind ourselves that the democracies of classical times were not like ours. They were based on slave labor, and directed by masters who knew their purpose. Slave labor has now disappeared, and ideally we like to think that democracy today means government by the representatives of the people by consent of the people. But many today also feel that the sovereign power, the people, has, through a process of negative democracy, abrogated its rights to a power elite, to a bureaucracy, to what you will, which is consciously determining the directions we follow. This, it seems to me, is again too simple. The element of the unknown in government increases with every step we are now taking to apply the fruits of science. If the basis of power is being changed, it is less by some governing body, however formed; and more and more by a process of applying scientific knowledge without any real possibility of determining its final consequences. Neither the voice of the majority, nor those through which it is expressed, can proclaim the precise lines of the future.

Scientists in Democracy

Where do scientists stand, as ordinary citizens, in this process whereby the application of the fruits of their discoveries can become a potential prison for our abstract liberties? It is argued that because of their special knowledge scientists can be aware of the danger and promise arising from their discoveries, and that therefore they have a special responsibility in relation to the most pressing problems of our time. I should agree with this, if it meant no more than that scientists are better able to appreciate the scientific facts, and that wise judgments on matters of policy in which scientific and technological considerations are a major issue are unlikely to be made merely by adding to secondhand appreciations of the technical and scientific aspects of the problem, assessments of the related political and economic factors. What is clearly needed in such cases is a direct sense of the scientific issues at stake. But how can the scientist as such, who is not responsible for its application, accept the responsibility for predicting some vast social transformation that might result from what seems an innocent observation at the time it is made? Scientists are the source of new scientific knowledge, but they are not necessarily visionaries, nor, in our particular world, do they occupy the seat of effective power.

But I should agree all the more if one coupled with this view of the scientist's responsibility the thought that in the problem of preserving our liberties lies the most important reason for regarding an education in science as now constituting an essential part of an education in the humanities. For if an understanding of social and political purpose is one of the aims of the liberal arts, then that aim cannot be realized until their scope is widened to embrace a proper understanding of the scientific knowledge, the application of which is now so rapidly transforming our intellectual and material environment.

Science, technology and humanism seem to have assumed that order of importance in the determination of our affairs. I do not know how it is in the rest of the world; but over the postwar years the changes which the tacit application of science and technology have occasioned in Great Britain seem far more profound than any that have been brought about through the overt discussion of social values or social goals. If this kind of thing is happening, can the humanities continue as a potent educational discipline without encompassing an understanding of the social forces which derive from the application of the natural sciences? Scientific literacy, we are told in a recently issued report on education, will need to be far more widespread than it is if we are to solve the problems of this age. Undoubtedly this is needed, but alone it is not a sufficient condition to ensure the solution of our problems—for here I agree with Aldous Huxley[10] that "higher education is not necessarily a guarantee of higher virtue or higher political wisdom." What we most need to learn is that in the big matters in which new scientific knowledge and technology are the major component, and which now affect human destiny, wise decisions for today cannot be safely taken unless we realize that those same decisions determine the shape of tomorrow and the day after. This realization may not lead to the right decisions; but it might help obviate some of the worse.

7

The Social Function of Science*

IT IS AN ODD THOUGHT THAT AS LITTLE AS TWENTY YEARS AGO many English scientists found the idea of science having a social function not only strange but even threatening. The concept is a truism today. How could it be otherwise now that science is maintained out of public funds on so much more massive a scale than we were accustomed to in the days before the Second World War? In those years, when science was usually supported on a shoestring, and was still very much of a personal venture, suggestions that it should become an ordered activity were bound to arouse strong passions and opposition. In England the debate came to a head in 1939 when that distinguished radical Professor J. D. Bernal[1] published his *Social Function of Science*, which was followed a little later by J. G. Crowther's[2] *Social Relations of Science*. Both authors made powerful pleas for the planned direction of scientific effort, and both had played a part in the establishment, in 1938, of a section of the British Association for the Advancement of Science to deal with the Social and International Relations of Science.

With the Second World War on us, I found Bernal's book a fascinating challenge. But I can well remember how some of my colleagues of the period feared that what Bernal wanted was to dragoon scientists into work which they would not necessarily wish to undertake, in the pursuit of ends of which they would

* The text of the Rickman Godlee Lecture, delivered at University College, London, in 1960.

not approve. I recall how one of them, a microanatomist who was an expert in the staining of tissues, remonstrated with me, perhaps not in all seriousness, about Bernal's presumed purpose. "Why," he exclaimed, "I know what he is after; he is going to tell me that I dare not ever again use gentian violet as a stain for my sections, and that from now on I shall have to restrict myself to methylene blue." No words of mine could persuade him that I was as ready as he to defend to the end our right to carry on with science as we knew it, and that no one was going to coerce me to undertake researches that I had not decided on myself; but that, knowing Bernal, I felt certain that he had no dictatorial ambitions, however extreme the effect his printed words might appear to some.

Freedom in Science

The reaction against the idea that science has a social responsibility soon crystallized in the formation of a group which called itself the Society for Freedom in Science. It thrived during the war years and in the immediate postwar period, and was responsible for a number of eloquent polemics[3] directed against scientists who were held to be animated by the desire to "organize" science. The movement died soon after the war, when it was realized that no one was going to browbeat British scientists into doing things against their will and for which they were not trained. Professor Michael Polanyi, who had played a leading part in the movement, tells the story in a footnote to the first chapter of his Logic of Liberty,[4] published in 1951.

In August 1938 the British Association for the Advancement of Science founded a new Division for the Social and International Relations of Science, which was largely motivated from the start by the desire to give deliberate social guidance to the progress of science. This movement gathered considerable momentum throughout the following years, so that when the Division met in December 1945 for a discussion on the Planning of Science, I expected the meeting to be overwhelmingly in favor of planning. My opening address, "The

Social Message of Pure Science," was written with this prospect in mind, but actually the occasion proved a turning point. Speakers and audience showed themselves consistently in favor of the traditional position of pure science, pursued freely for its own sake. Since then, the movement for the planning of science has rapidly declined to insignificance in Britain.

All this seems to imply that Professor Polanyi, and others who thought like him, had to some extent been tilting at windmills. A few may genuinely have conjured up an image of scientific slavery.[5] To others who were opposed to any thought of the planning of scientific activity, the bugbear was the word "planning." What Professor Polanyi himself was concerned about was the preservation of the freedom and liberty of the individual in science, and in this aim there can have been very few scientists who were not his allies.

Nonetheless, there was a major confusion, and a real tangle of crossed purposes. Polanyi was wrong in believing that by 1945 the planning of science was "already declining into insignificance in Britain." But his belief that this was happening is very important, and underlines the issue which I propose examining in this chapter. What I want to discuss are certain differences that can now be perceived between the concept of the social function of science as viewed by those who wrote on the subject in the later 1930s, and what I personally understand the term to mean today. These differences do not arise simply because the intervening years have seen the emergence of a new world of technological wonders. The issue is more fundamental, and ultimately concerns not just an appreciation of the social function of science, but a realization of the social and political limitations of scientists. In what sense, I find myself asking, were people using the term "function" in 1939? Is there a social function of science, has science "social relations," in the sense that scientists in their capacity as scientists have an obligation to cast their thoughts to the usefulness or otherwise of their work and discoveries to the society in which they live? Or has science a social function in the same sense that one may write that it is a function or characteristic of a cat that it eats mice? Is the term "social function" something that carries with it the sense of obligation, or is it merely an attribute or aspect of scientific knowledge?

A Directed Function?

Bernal clearly saw the term in the first light. We have "to consider the social function not absolutely," as he believed, "but as something which has grown up imperceptibly with the growth of science." He saw science—in the same way as most of us see it today—as an activity which results in both the extension and the organization of knowledge, and with the application of the fruits of knowledge, hopefully to human welfare. To him both of these functions—the gathering of knowledge and the application of knowledge—were the responsibility of scientists. But, as he saw it, the two proceeded in so uncoordinated and haphazard a way as to result in "a structure of appalling inefficiency, both as to its internal organization and as to the means of application to problems of production or of welfare."

In a book which still has far more than historical value, he then went on to analyze the way scientific advances take place, and how they are planned, whether we regard science as an adventure into pure thought, or as the instrument which generates social wealth. He dealt with scientific organization and training, as well as with problems relating to the application and exploitation of scientific discovery. And he ended with the general and Marxist conclusion—possibly the one which was responsible for stimulating most of the reaction against the book as a whole—that the possibilities which science offers can be realized only by creating "a new ordered and integrated political and economic system on a world scale." To Bernal the ultimate implication of science was that of "unified and coordinated and, above all, conscious control of the whole of social life."

I have reread the chapter in which this thought appears with the same interest that it evoked in me twenty years ago. Bernal saw science as the instrument through which starvation, disease, slavery and war could be eliminated from our midst. To him, it was utterly anomalous that a highly developed science could stand "almost isolated from a traditional literary culture." As he put it, "no culture can stand indefinitely apart from the dominating practical ideas of the time, without degenerating into pedantic futility."

But whether or not one agrees with Bernal's views about the way science was being frustrated in the period of the world's history about which he was writing, or with his views about the social framework within which science could thrive—one did not need to believe in order to listen—I find myself returning inevitably to his assertion that science implies a conscious control of the whole of social life. Even if science is the greatest force which is determining the shape and nature of our material world, can it really be said to provide a "conscious" control in the sense that Bernal argued so eloquently twenty years ago?

The Nature of Scientific Activity

In those days we spoke about fundamental or basic science and applied science. For many the distinction which the two terms imply is still both adequate and sufficient. It is based mainly "on the time interval that separates the acquirement of knowledge from its effects in practice. A fundamental scientific discovery may take anything from twenty to one hundred years before it influences the lives of the majority of people. A particular scientific study of some manufacturing process may, on the other hand, be effective in production in as many days."[6]

Basic research has, of course, always been the chief source of the big advances that have occurred in scientific knowledge. It is also—space and nuclear science apart—the least costly and, at the same time, the freest area of science. What costs the money and what is the most far-reaching in its immediate social effects is the application of a scientific discovery to some practical end.

During the twenty years that have elapsed since Bernal's book appeared—twenty years made up of five years of war and fifteen years of peace—we have seen the volume of scientific knowledge grow at a rate faster than any of us could have imagined, and with it the numbers of scientists and engineers. We have seen science applied at an ever accelerating speed. We have also seen science spread in one way or another into amost every field of human interest, even to the extent that some of us may have doubts about the existence of those two distinct cultures whose separation, however real it may have been twenty years ago, perhaps hardly deserved so powerful an emphasis as was accorded it by Sir Charles Snow[7] when he reanimated Bernal's theme in his Rede lecture.

At the end of the thirties, that is to say in the days immediately preceding the outbreak of the Second World War, the best available estimate was that the total sum spent on academic, industrial and government research in Great Britain each year was no more than about seven million pounds—roughly .1 percent of the Gross National Product. At the end of the fifties we were spending on all aspects of science twenty times as much in real terms, nearly 500 million pounds a year, or approximately 2 percent of our Gross National Product.*

With the government contributing from public funds fully 300 million pounds to this vast sum,† the simple subdivision of science into basic and applied no longer seems to be an adequate definition of scientific activity. The administration of science, even its planning, has become much more important today than ever before, contrary to whatever impression Professor Polanyi may have had about what was going to happen. Deciding on the apportionment of scientific resources has made it useful[8] to try to separate the kind of fundamental or pure basic research which is not directed to any particular goal of possible application, and which is concerned basically with the increase in our knowledge of the nature of the material world, from the fundamental but "objective" research which has some clear purpose in view because it is carried out in some field of recognized potential

* The estimate for 1965 is 750 million pounds.
† In 1965 the figure was nearly 500 million pounds, divided equally between Civil and Defense Research and Development.

technological importance. We also have to distinguish both of these kinds of fundamental research from those technological activities called applied research and development. Applied research takes the fruits of fundamental research and shows how they can be used for some precise end; while development takes the results of applied research in the devising of some new machine or system of machines, or some new process of production, which will be better than whatever it was designed to replace.

It is useful to explore further the distinction between these various aspects of scientific activity. This will help us understand how science achieves a utilitarian social value as opposed to the more cultural one which the growth of knowledge implies in itself. It will also show that there is a real difference between the planning of scientific activity on the one hand and the social function of science, whether or not we associate with the term a sense of obligation, on the other.

Science and Technology

I shall begin by turning to another of Professor Polanyi's works,[9] in which he provides a useful analysis of the difference between basic science and "technology." Technology, he writes, teaches action, but "only actions to be undertaken for *material* advantages by the use of *implements* according to (more or less) *specifiable* rules" or "operational principles." The difference between scientific knowledge on the one hand, and an operational principle of technology on the other, is assured, as Polanyi reminds us, by patent law, there being "a sharp distinction between a *discovery*, which makes an addition to our knowledge of nature, and an *invention*, which establishes a new operational principle serving some acknowledged advantage." Both demand the quality of originality, but in science this resides "in the power of seeing more deeply than others into the nature of things, while in technology (i.e., *invention*) it consists in the ingenuity of the artificer in turning known facts to a surprising advantage."

As Polanyi goes on to point out, it is of the essence of technology that an invention "should be economic, and thus achieve a material advantage. . . . Any invention can be rendered worthless and, indeed, farcical by a radical change in the values of the means used up and the ends produced by it." Inventions succeed each other because it is assumed that the next one is always better. Tramcars replaced horse-drawn buses, and tramcars are, in turn, being replaced by motorbuses and the motorcar. But if, to use another of Polanyi's illustrations, "the price of all fuel went up one hundredfold, all steam engines, gas turbines, motorcars and airplanes would have to be thrown on the junk heap." Sometimes "inventions" follow each other so fast that one may swallow its predecessor, in effect, before, in terms of Polanyi's analogy, the price of fuel has gone up. In the world of weapon technology, there is a saying that "if it works, it's obsolete."

Accelerating the Applications of Science

I think I can illustrate Polanyi's distinction between science and technology, at the same time as I help bridge the gap between him and Bernal, by reference to a piece of personal history.

In the thirties, and well into the period of the war, there existed a small dining club, of which I happened to be the convener, called the "Tots and Quots"—an abbreviation and inversion of the tag *quot homines, tot sententiae*—to mark the fact that its twenty members, of whom Bernal was one, not only represented a very wide spectrum of opinion and experience, but also very rarely agreed with each other. We met, as a rule, monthly, and at the end of our dinners a free discussion on some selected general topic would be opened, with discussion and argument often continuing until midnight. When the war began, our main concern became the problem of mobilizing science for the war effort, and our exchanges were usually helped by various guests, including ministers and military authorities.

At the end of one such dinner, which took place in July, 1940, when the battle for France was raging, Allen Lane, the founder of Penguin Books, who had come along as a guest, remarked that it was a pity that the substance of our discussion had not been recorded, since it would have made an interesting Penguin. We took him up immediately and asked whether he would undertake to produce the book in the space of two weeks if we succeeded in getting him the full text within the next fortnight. He accepted the challenge. So did we. Some pretty vigorous organizing, writing and spurring then took place, and after, as I well recall, two or three days and nights in which one or two of us worked nonstop, we were able to get Lane the text of the book. Two weeks later we dined again, and there at each cover was a copy of a paperback entitled *Science in War*.[10]

Essentially the book, which was published anonymously, dealt with the problem of speeding the translation of scientific discovery into matters of practical value for the war.[11] At the time, all of us felt strongly that not enough use was being made by those in whose hands our destinies lay, either of scientific knowledge or of scientific methods of operation, or, indeed, of scientists. There was no question here of any theoretical separation of basic from applied science, but only a sense of urgency about the need to shorten the period by which the two were bridged, in the interests of winning the war. Not surprisingly for the period in which it appeared, there was an implied assumption that all science has a practical function, and that none of it could not be put to use. We did not address our book to scientists, but to a public, and a governmental machine, which we believed was not fully informed about what science meant to the country, and about the ways it could help in the war effort.

The Situation Today

Twenty years later, public opinion in the United Kingdom is utterly different.[12] We have—to start at the top—a Minister for Education and Science. In a debate on scientific policy which took place in the House of Lords on November 9, 1959, the opener began with the following statement: "A country's wealth and power are today largely determined by the extent of its scientific knowledge and its capacity to use that knowledge," adding: "this seems to me to be a pretty clear statement behind social principles which I hope will not lead to political division . . . even though they carry some recognition of the need for planning."[13]

To one who has been long concerned with what I can call Whitehall views about science, this sentence implies a fantastic change over the past twenty years in the climate of opinion about "the social function of science." But how, indeed, could it be otherwise? Whether we talk about the social function or the social relations of science, it remains a fact that the physical changes which have characterized the past twenty years of the world's social history have been due more to the direct and indirect application of science than to any other factor.

America, Britain and other parts of the earth live in what we now hear called "the affluent society." There is certainly no doubt about the physical affluence which the Western world enjoys today, as compared with twenty years ago. There is also, as Galbraith[14] pointed out in the book which gave the term "affluent society" so wide a currency, a great deal of reciprocal squalor. As world population grows, the application of science through technology is bound to mean greater wealth in some parts of the world and relatively less in others. Science, we all realize, may, in fact, be increasing the gap which has always existed between the "haves" and the "have-nots." But, on the other hand, both the poor and the rich can be relied upon to go on seeking for the application of science in order to satisfy their wants, as either their numbers or their appetites grow.

Over the twenty years since the anonymous *Science in War* appeared, the agricultural and mineral resources of the world have been developed to an unprecedented extent. Deserts have been made to blossom. Previously uninhabited regions of the Arctic and sub-Arctic are now the homes of communities organized in the ways of an industrial society. New materials have been provided through the application of chemical knowledge—nylon, terylene, a host of plastics all designed to fill different needs. New sources of energy have been developed. And under the threat of cheap nuclear power, the more conventional sources, such as coal-fired power stations, coal-gas generators and oil have also become more scientifically and efficiently used. Under the threat which this resurrection of old industry constitutes, we can have no doubt, too, that, as the years pass, ways will be found for reducing the cost of nuclear power. And wherever we look behind these conspicuous material advances, we see an increasing urge to more literacy, to more education and, in particular, to more education in science.

The benefits of the new world of science may not spread evenly across the face of the globe. But whatever further disequilibrium their spread entails—with population multiplying without restraint in some parts of the world, and with technology making even greater leaps forward in others—spread it will.

Science Policy

Most countries of the world, including the United Kingdom, have organized, or are organizing, a potent machinery for helping the spread. This is the age of Science Policy. We in the U.K. have our Council on Scientific Policy, our University Grants Committee, our Research Councils and our fifty or so research associations in which industry and government combine to see what scientific knowledge can be transformed into industrial technology and so into greater productivity and wealth.[15] The United States has its corresponding institutions, with the President's Science Committee and the National Science Foundation at the center. In the U.S.S.R., the Soviet Academy of Sciences has overriding and executive power in the fields of pure and applied science, administering some ninety research institutions which among them employ a professional staff of over 11,000. France, Italy and India, as well as countries which have grown to independence as recently as Ghana, all have their own institutions to plan scientific policy.

Those who, like Professor Polanyi, saw the planning of science as something which was bound to become insignificant, could not have been more mistaken. This planning is necessary—regardless of the political framework in which it takes place—for the simple reason that the scale of the social resources employed in science and technology has increased so vastly over the past two decades. And it is likely to go on increasing. What we have to try to ensure is that the planning of scientific activity does not lead to the regimentation of the scientist, however regimented the enterprises—such as nuclear and space science—in which scientists may engage.

In my view, the institutions of science, the research councils and advisory councils are only the instruments, not the motive power, behind the growth and application of science. They no more determine the social function—or let me better call it, the social aspect—of science than they are able to dictate where the next major scientific discovery is to be made. What then constitutes the motive power behind the growth and applications of science?

Motive Powers in the Scientific Process

So far as pure fundamental science is concerned, it is merely the intellectual challenge and pleasure the individual scientist experiences in extending the bounds of general scientific knowledge. In the case of applied science, the motive power is clearly constituted by all those forces which lie behind the growth of our "affluent society," and which were so vividly described by Galbraith. We can see, for example, that the applications of scientific knowledge provided the means of mass communication—the modern newspaper, the film, the radio, the television set through which the fruits of science could be advertised. Even darkest Africa will tomorrow be illuminated by the TV screen, as it is already filled with the articulate noises of thousands of radios. Those who do not know today what the other man is enjoying will certainly know tomorrow.

In a statement[16] which a large British company published to mark the tercentenary of the Royal Society, we read that "a technological achievement does not stand by itself. It can be understood only if it is regarded in the context of its history. It stretches back through salesmanship, production, design, to the scientific work which made the achievement possible; it reaches forward into social and economic changes which follow the achievement . . . a factory making electric generators, for example, cannot be understood in isolation. Its activity begins in schools and technical colleges and university laboratories, where ideas germinate and interests are formed, and its influence can be followed after the generators are installed: into Indian villages, emancipating the people from poverty and dissolving the constraints of caste; into the minds of Africans, detribalizing them and molding their ideas into patterns of the twentieth century; into the Arab world, equipping it with tools for its resurgent nationalism; into the industrial towns of Britain, creating new opportunities for employment and new conditions for family life. It is no wonder that industry has become one of the patrons of learning. The technologist is irrevocably involved in mankind." And the passage ends by saying: "This is no sentimental involvement, no woolly gesture of goodwill toward boffins and sociologists."

That we can now all agree with. We are dealing with the plain facts of life.

Those who generate wealth through trade, and those who have been concerned, without thought of material gain, to alleviate suffering and to spread knowledge and literacy, have provided, and will continue to provide, the force which imparts to scientific knowledge its social aspect. TV, we are told, is depriving shoppers of their capacity to exercise discretion in what they buy; but it is making them buy, and it is making industry hum. Equally, the spread of knowledge in dark places often provides that sense of injustice, of frustration and, at the same time, of hope, which lies behind the nationalist movements which are passing like a vast wave over the world. Waddington[17] is not exaggerating when he writes that "the

major political force which is shaping man's history in our time
is the conviction . . . that to die at eighty after a healthy life
using inanimate sources of power is, in some real and undeniable
sense, better than to die at forty after a life of back-breaking
labor, hunger and sickness."

Do scientists, one may therefore ask, help significantly in
determining the directions in which science is applied? The
answer is manifestly "yes." However little they may have been
concerned with the conscious control of the whole of social life
—I quote Bernal's phrase—the energies of *most* men who are
trained as professional scientists have certainly been focused on
the application of the fruits of basic scientific research. It was
the scientist, for example, who realized the immense power that
lay in the application of antibiotic action, and who, by so doing,
helped transform the whole spectrum of disease—even though
those engaged in manufacture and commerce may have helped
determine the outcome. It was the scientist who discovered the
pesticidal properties of substances such as D.D.T., and who
urged that they should be used for the suppression of the
malaria-carrying mosquito. His voice had clearly to be heard
before the manufacturer and the advertiser could come on the
scene. It was the scientist and the applied scientist who blazed
the trail for broadcasting and television companies. It was the
scientist who not only opened up the field of nuclear physics,
but showed how an atom bomb could be made, and how electric
power could be provided from nuclear fuels. And at the start it
was the scientist and the engineer who argued that we should
divert resources into the promotion of space technology and
space science.

The space scientist is just like every other kind of scientist in
urging the claims of his own special field of interest. And since
science is now so big, and since hardly any scientist knows what
happens outside his own particular field, the pressures which all
scientists bring to bear in devising the social aspects of science
are inevitably uncoordinated.

There is no limit to the amount of scientific research and

development that could be done—I am not claiming, of course, that there is no limit to the "good" scientific research that is possible. The United Kingdom now spends, as I have said, about 500 million pounds on research and development, somewhat more than 2 percent of our Gross National Product.* The United States spends the equivalent of not quite 4,000† million pounds—a figure close to 3 percent of the American G.N.P. One has to realize that figures of this magnitude are arbitrary in the sense that the applied scientist, particularly the applied scientist who is concerned with the defense services of his country, could show many ways in which they could be multiplied. In this kind of activity, every view that counts is an expert's view; and every expert is expert about something different. The way the social function or social aspect of science becomes evident, or manifests itself, is basically through the interaction of a diversity of uncoordinated expert views.

The way we now divide up the resources that we devote to scientific research and development represents the accretion of past empirical decisions, and hardly accords with some other pattern of expenditure which might conceivably be followed if we were to start afresh. Even so, I find it difficult to believe that we shall ever be able to decide about the disbursement of our scientific resources by use of some administrative principle dramatically different from the one which determines our actions today. The present balance of knowledge within science was determined by the interaction of innumerable strokes of genius, each to greater or lesser degree unpredictable in its timing and repercussions. There is no ideal and universal balance of scientific activity to which we can direct our sights.

Scientists and Social Policy

Here my opinions clash sharply with those of scientists who feel that scientists as a body could play a bigger and more

* In 1965 about £750 million. £500 was the 1960 figure.
† In 1965 closer to £7,500 million.

prescient part than they yet do in the determination of science policy and social policy.[18] But this point seems to be trivial in comparison with the issue which I elaborated in the preceding chapter. While science necessitates absolute freedom from restraint if it is to progress, and while it cannot be prevented from being revolutionary—to overthrow tomorrow what seems certain today—it determines in an increasingly unpredictable way the main issues about which all of us exercise our freedom of choice within society. History has shown over and over again that it is the unpredictable social consequences of the scientific applications of today which determine the social environment of tomorrow. In my view, a scientist is still no better at predicting the changes which are likely to occur than is the next man, even though he is obviously more aware of the nature of the facts that bring about the changes.[19]

This, I know, is not everybody's view. Sir Charles Goodeve, a distinguished Fellow of University College,[20] and one who has been much concerned to see how the methods of science can be used to solve social problems, has been fashioning another. In a recent address,[21] he tells us that, while scientists are held to be responsible for altering the lives of people, and for increasing their powers to destroy each other, they have been content to leave others to solve most of the social problems of which ultimately they have been the cause. He rightly points out that scientists have, in general, been reluctant to respond to the challenge of finding out more about the social repercussions of their work—in spite of the limited but occasionally conspicuous success of operational-research workers since the Second World War ended. He suggests that surveys of public attitudes, which have been so helpful in the field of market and consumer research, could provide governments with a powerful weapon in discharging their responsibilities of dealing with social organization. And he expresses the hope that society itself should become the subject of real scientific study.

If I understand him fully, what he is implying is that a proper investigation of the factors which lead to decisions being taken by groups of people will help provide society with a better means than it possesses now for deciding what its future should be.

Much as I hope that he is right, I fear that I am not as optimistic as he is. Market research may tell the manufacturer which way to package a particular kind of soap. The way he advertises his soap may help him impose his will on his potential customers. But a particular piece of market research and a particular study of how people are reacting at a given moment can only be regarded as relating to the circumstances under review—as a finite phase of conditioning of one single aspect of behavior. What I fear is that surveys of public attitudes, the world of market research, advertisement and polls may help produce an environment of conventional attitude without telling how people would behave about *completely new and important* things the day after tomorrow. Is everybody certain today that as a result of yesterday's poll Mr. Kennedy has been elected President of the United States?[22] More important, the majority of us are hardly likely to use the results of past Gallup polls and ballots to tell us who Mr. Kennedy's successor in office is going to be four years hence. The natural history constituted by this kind of social science has surely a long way to go before it becomes a predictive science.

Nonetheless, I hope that what Sir Charles Goodeve is talking about will thrive and become a predictive and operational science, and that it will become possible for human social judgment to be aided by studies of the kind he advocates, in the same way as human action has been made easier through the steam engine and internal-combustion machine, and in the same way as routine human decision has been made easier through the development of electronics and computers. There are great possibilities at this level of operation. But it is not the level of novel social judgment.

For example, we are told that "electronic brains" can now be devised, or have been devised, into whose "memory stores" so much information can be fed about the rules of chess that a robot could be relied upon to beat the average chess player. We know, too, that at the present moment teams of American research workers are perfecting an instrument which will be able to translate the Russian language into English at speeds far greater than that of an experienced Russian translator. And less than a month ago I read in an American newspaper that the day when an electronic brain will be able to diagnose our complaints and perhaps write our prescriptions is much closer than we think.

But while I recognize that all these developments are on the way, and that more of them will surface, I doubt whether we shall ever be able to rely upon machines to replace human judgment in the really important areas of social decision. For, however much the machine can accelerate and extend certain human mental processes, the permutations and combinations of its operations are restricted to the postulates and pieces of information that have been fed into it. Polanyi[23] has put the matter very clearly: "A man's mind can carry out feats of intelligence *by aid of* a machine and also *without* such aid, while a machine can function only as an extension of a person's body under the control of his mind." When I quote him in this context, it is irrelevant to ask what he means by "mind" and what he means by "machine," and whether his use of these two terms is one which would stand up to a final logical analysis.

The simple fact remains that, while the machine can make precise and probably even more certain judgments in areas of operation which have known and given dimensions, it cannot operate creatively where its terms of reference have not been defined in an articulate way. And that, to my mind, is the essence of human social judgment.

A Divergence of Views

Having said this, I must now try to summarize my views of the differences, as I see them, between my own concept of the social function of science today and that which inspired the British Association twenty years ago. As I have said, the three

essential issues which emerged from Bernal's analysis—which I
shall regard here as exemplifying the then British Association
view—were, first, that advances in scientific knowledge and the
application of this knowledge were being frustrated because of a
lack of adequate support and adequate machinery; second, that
only through the applications of science could starvation, disease
and slavery be alleviated and the prospect of future war be
erased; and, third, that science implies a unified and coordinated,
and above all, a conscious control of the whole of social life, and
one which should be fitted into an appropriate political pattern.

When we look at the changes which have occurred since those
days, we can agree completely that the planning and support of
science in the 1930s were woefully inefficient. New scientific
institutions have since emerged and now flourish, and I have no
doubt that more will be born. We recognize only too well that
our own apparatus for administering and encouraging science is
still far from perfect, and that it constantly needs reexamina-
tion.[24]

There can also be no doubt about Bernal's second point. The
developments of the past twenty years show only too clearly that
without the further application of science, man's physical lot
cannot be improved. It is worth reflecting that antibiotics,
nuclear power, plastics, electronic engineering, radar, jet air
travel and a host of other similar things are all the fruit of the
past two decades. The automatic incorporation of scientific ideas
into our culture, and the physical application of these ideas are
now a far more potent force than any other in the transformation of society. There is no obvious limit to the marvels of
science.

But if the experience of the past twenty years reinforces everything that has ever been said about the material implications of
the phrase "the social function of science," I doubt very much
whether it has shown that science implies a conscious control of
our social life.

It must be plain to everybody that the ways of science, the
accidents that have determined the applications of scientific

discovery, and the unpredictable consequences of these applications, have been singularly independent of the different political frameworks of those countries of the West and East which have been most concerned to foster science. Science has gone ahead and been applied in precisely the same way in the West as in the East. What is more, a scientific development in one of the two world camps is in these days merely a challenge to better that same development in the other. The race to get man into space is only one example of this curious phenomenon which marks our present culture.[25]

The tercentenary celebrations of the Royal Society provoked some nostalgic sentiments about the powerful part played by the founders of the Society in the political and social world of their time, as compared with that which scientists play today. In one book,[26] in which an excellent account is given of six founders of the Society—including John Wilkins, Robert Boyle, Christopher Wren and Isaac Newton—we are told that not only have present British scientists lost ground in political influence and cultural versatility, but that, as a result of a lack of interest, the ideological and social problems of science, which ought to have been explored and solved during the previous three centuries, have been almost forgotten.

I fear that it is crying for the moon to suppose that any single scientist, or any small group of scientists, could today represent what the founders of the Royal Society did in their time. In 1660 the population of Great Britain was one-fifth of its present size; in large part it was illiterate; industry had hardly begun; and our international commitments and involvements represented a series of problems of a much lesser order of magnitude than those which have to be dealt with now. Try as I can, I cannot see how science today can be regarded as exercising a special active social function, in the sense of a conscious effort on the part of scientists to handle the social and political problems of our times.

We are in a period of transition. Even though nations multiply in number, all are inevitably moving, through the applications of science, to less diversified patterns of national interest than prevailed in past centuries. Whatever our respective histories, and whatever the stage of industrialization in which nations today find themselves, we all more and more want the same things. Trade, the speed of travel, the freedom of communications, are leading inevitably to a world which shares one general culture. The rate at which we can reach that goal—if accident does not prevent us from so doing—is not going to be determined by the edict of any one scientist or of any group of scientists. On the other hand, scientists can play a part. So long as our lives are determined through the deliberations of democratic institutions, so long can scientists, if they wish, play a part in the process.

But I repeat—a scientist is as yet no better equipped to predict the consequences of the applications of scientific advances than is the next cultivated man. On the other hand, because of their professional knowledge, scientists are in a better position than others to appreciate the nature of what it is that is bringing about social transformations. And that, in my view, is the best argument there is for greater scientific literacy—without which I fear we shall never be able to appreciate properly the ever-expanding social aspect of science. It is in that sense only that I see science having an active and effective social function.

Notes and References

1. AN UNEASY ALLIANCE

1. Dwight D. Eisenhower, *Public Papers of the President*, 1960–61, p. 1038 (United States Government Printing Office).

2. A. S. Parkes, "The Sex-Ratio in Human Populations," in *Man and His Future*, ed. Gordon Wolstenholme (London: Churchill, 1963).

   Dr. Parkes suggests that the explanation for this phenomenon is, first, that there is always a large excess of males over females at the time of conception; second, that there is a preponderance of males to females among the many embryos and foetuses which fail to survive until the time of birth; third, that prenatal mortality is higher in older than younger women; and, fourth, that the age of marriage falls during wars, and with it the incidence of prenatal mortality. In consequence, one would expect the ratio of male to female births to increase during wars.

3. J. G. Crowther, *The Social Relations of Science* (London: Macmillan, 1941).

   J. D. Bernal, *Science in History* (London: Watts, 1965).

4. J. D. Bernal, *The Social Function of Science* (London: Routledge, 1939).

5. N. Skentelbury, *History of the Ordnance Board*, Part I (London: Ordnance Board, 1965).

6. J. D. Bernal, *The Social Function of Science* (London: Routledge, 1939).

   Galileo, for example, was Professor of Military Science at the

161

University of Pavia and sold his invention of the telescope to the Venetian Signory "solely on account of its value in naval warfare." It was not a straightforward sale. The telescope was given to the Doge as a free gift in return for 1,000 ducats and a professorship for life. In his letter to the Doge he wrote:

> I have made a telescope, a thing for every maritime and terrestrial affair and an undertaking of inestimable worth. One is able to discover enemy sails and fleets at a greater distance than customary, so that we can discover him (the enemy) two hours or more before he discovers us, and by distinguishing the number and quality of the vessels, judge of his force whether to set out to chase him, or to fight, or to run away. . . . Also, on land one can look into the squares, buildings and defenses of the enemy from some distant vantage point and even in open country see and distinguish particularly to our great advantage all his movements and preparations. There are besides many other uses, clearly remarked by any person with judgment. And so, considering it worthy of being received by your Serenity and esteemed as useful, I have determined to present it to you and leave to you the decision about this discovery—ordering and providing according to what seems opportune to your prudence, whether or not it be manufactured.

According to Bernal, "the great technical developments of the eighteenth and nineteenth centuries, particularly the large-scale smelting of iron by means of coal, and the introduction of the steam engine, were directly due to the needs for artillery which the increasingly large scale of war demanded. The accurate boring of steam-engine cylinders, which made all the difference in practice between the efficient engines of Watt and the earlier atmospheric engines, was due to the improvements introduced by Wilkinson, who was able to make them on account of his experience in the boring of cannon. From the same field comes Rumford's discovery of the mechanical equivalent of heat, which was to furnish the basic theory for all heat engines."

7. Sir John H. Briggs, *Naval Administrations 1827–1892*, ed. Lady Briggs (London: Sampson Low, Marston & Co., 1897).

8. Brian Connell, *Manifest Destiny* (London: Cassell, 1953).

9. See B. H. Liddell Hart, *Foch* (London: Eyre & Spottiswoode, 1931).

10. Ladislas d'Orcy, "The War Has Modified the Airplane," *Scientific American*, 113, 196.

11. "The essential basis of the military life is the ordered application of force under an unlimited liability," a clause in the "unwritten contract" of the soldier.
Sir John Hackett, *The Profession of Arms* (London: Times Publishing Company, 1962).

12. A. S. Eve, *Rutherford* (Cambridge University Press, 1939).

13. *Report of the Committee on the Management and Control of Reseach and Development* (London: H.M.S.O., 1961). It has, of course, always been difficult to define precisely what we mean by "pure" or "basic" science, and what we mean by "applied" science. An attempt to provide definitions was made by the above Committee. "Pure or basic research" was described as "research carried out solely in order to increase scientific knowledge, that is, knowledge of the nature of the material world." Another term in common use for pure or basic is "fundamental," and all three words are "usually connected with the idea of work of high intellectual quality," even though every working scientist knows that a fair amount of "pure" scientific research is often of a routine or of a preliminary nature. This kind of research, which the individual research worker selects in order to satisfy his own intellectual curiosity, was differentiated by the Committee from another category, which was called "objective basic research." This was defined as "basic research in fields of recognized potential technological importance." The difference between "pure basic" and "objective basic" researches derives mainly from the fact that the latter is stimulated primarily by technological needs. "It, therefore, calls for a planned approach even when the satisfaction of these needs is remote." Applied research was described as "work carried out in order to achieve a practical goal which can be fairly precisely defined, such as a new process or piece of equipment."

14. P. B. Medawar, "Anglo-Saxon Attitudes," *Encounter*, 25, 52 (1965).

15. J. C. Dancy, "Technology in a Liberal Education," *Advancement of Science*, 22 (100), 379 (1965).

16. C. P. Snow, *The Two Cultures: A Second Look* (Cambridge University Press, 1964).

17. C. P. Snow, *Science and Government* (London: Oxford University Press, 1961).
Earl of Birkenhead, *The Prof in Two Worlds* (London: Collins, 1961).

18. Medical Research Council. Special Report No. 8 (1917).

19. E. Rutherford, Obituary of Henry Gwyn Jeffreys Moseley, *Nature*, 96, 33 (1915).

20. M. M. Postan, D. Hay and J. D. Scott, *Design and Development of Weapons* (London: H.M.S.O. and Longmans, Green & Co., 1964).

21. W. S. Churchill, *Second World War*, Vol. III (London: Cassell, 1950).

22. Margaret Gowing, *Britain and Atomic Energy, 1939–1945* (London: Macmillan, 1964).

23. W. W. Tarn, *Alexander the Great: I. Narrative* (Cambridge University Press, 1951).

24. H. W. Turnbull (ed.), *The Correspondence of Isaac Newton* (Cambridge University Press, 1961), III, 364.

25. B. H. Liddell Hart, in *Thoughts on War* (London: Faber & Faber, 1944).

26. Robert Watson-Watt, *Advancement of Science*, IV (1948), 320.

27. *Ibid.*

28. S. Zuckerman, "The Need for Operational Research," in *Operational Research in Practice* (London: Pergamon, 1958).

29. *The Strategic Air War Against Germany, 1939–1945*, Report of British Bombing Survey Unit (1947).

30. Hilary St. George Saunders, *Royal Air Force 1939–1945*, Vol. III. *The Fight Is Won* (London: H.M.S.O., 1954).
Charles Webster and Noble Frankland, *The Strategic Air Offensive Against Germany, 1939–1945*, Vol. III (London: H.M.S.O., 1961).
Gordon A. Harrison, *Cross-Channel Attack*. United States Army in World War II. (Washington, D.C.: Office of the Chief of Military History, 1951).

31. Alfred North Whitehead, *Adventures of Ideas* (New York: Macmillan, 1933).

32. J. Johnston, "The Science of Prediction and Discrimination," *Guardian*, August 17, 1965.

33. F. T. Samuelson, "Summer Jitters or Genuine Weakness," *Financial Times*, June 8, 1965.

34. Sir Archibald Wavell, *Generals and Generalship* (The Lees Knowles Lectures, 1939. Reprinted by the Times Publishing Company, 1941).

2. THE IMPACT OF TECHNOLOGY

1. Dwight D. Eisenhower, *Public Papers of the President, 1960–61*, p. 1038 (United States Government Printing Office).

2. Charles Singer, *History of Technology*, Vol. V (Oxford University Press, 1954–58).
   C. Gibb, and A. Briggs, *History of Birmingham* (Published for for the Birmingham City Council by Oxford University Press, 1952).

3. *The Economic Impact of Defense and Disarmament* (Washington, D.C.: U.S. Government Printing Office, July, 1965), 20402.

4. C. Freeman and A. Young, *The Research and Development Effort in Western Europe, North America and the Soviet Union* (Organization for Economic Co-operation and Development).
   See also Ian Low, "The R. and D. Race," *New Scientist, 28*, 817 (1965).

5. Jerome Wiesner and Herbert F. York, "National Security and the Nuclear Test Ban," *Scientific American, 211* (4), 27 (1964).

6. Kenneth W. Gatland, "What Price Anti-Missile Missiles," *New Scientist, 28*, 636 (1965).

7. *Report of the Committee on Arms Control and Disarmament* (Washington, D.C.: The White House Conference on International Cooperation, 1965).

8. Hansard, April 6, 1965, cols. 280, 319.

9. President Kennedy in *Washington Post*, December 25, 1962.

10. United States Department of Defense Press Release, July 28, 1965.

11. Hansard, December 14, 1964, col. 39.

12. Hansard, December 16, 1964, col. 419.
    The Prime Minister:

    > Taking first our own expenditure in money and in resources on defense programs, whether of manpower or equipment, the plain fact is that we have been trying to do too much. The result has been gravely to weaken our economic strength and independence without producing viable defenses. Planned defense expenditure in the present year represents 7.1 percent of our Gross National Product. This is a higher figure than in any other major Western country, with the exception of the United States.
    >
    > There is built into our defense systems an unavoidable rate of increase—in the absence of changes of policy—which will mean, year by year, a crippling increase in the call on money and on resources. My right hon. friend the Minister of Defense for the Army the other day gave some alarming figures, which I do not think will be disputed, about the immediate rise that is ahead of us in the cost of equipping various Army units. Here there is an inexorable law that in terms of military expenditure the rise in costs is rising far faster than any conceivable increase in the Gross National Product.

13. This point is discussed in a more general context in the essay "Liberty in the Age of Science," republished as Chapter 6 of this volume.

14. *Report of the Committee of Inquiry into the Aircraft Industry* under the Chairmanship of Lord Plowden (H.M.S.O., December, 1965), cmd. 2853.

15. John Rubel, "Trends in Research and Development" (Address given December 4, 1963, University of California, Los Angeles). See also David Allison, "The Civilian Technology Lag," *Science and Technology*, **24,** 24 (1963).

16. The same point is made in an illuminating analysis of the nature and results of "Research and Development in Electronic Capital Goods," published in the *National Institute Economic Review*, No. 34 (Nov., 1965), in which we are reminded that "both in America and Britain some firms which have concen-

trated on the military market and have the largest military research and development contracts have a less satisfactory record
in the civil market and as exporters. Thus the supposed benefits
of American government programs are not so straightforward as
appears at first sight." On the other hand, every progressive
firm in the industry must have "a minimum level of research
and development work in progress," this minimum or threshold
being "an *absolute* level of resources, not a *ratio* of sales." It
is here that "American military and space programs have undoubtedly given some competitive advantages to the U.S. components industry"—but instances where this leads to a new or
improved product with civil applications are not typical. The
analysis concludes firmly that it is no way to counter American
domination of the world civil market for electronic capital
goods by mounting military and space development programs
on the American scale, but given that "the main priority is
economic growth, then the American advantage can probably
best be offset by much more ambitious civil research and development projects"—i.e., not to rely on "fallout" from military
programs.

17. See J. D. Bernal, *Science in History* (London: Watts, 1965).

18. Derek de Solla Price, "The Scientific Foundations of Science
    Policy," *Nature*, 206, 233 (1965).

19. C. N. Hinshelwood, "Science and Scientists," *Advancement of
    Science*, 22, 347 (1965).

20. Michael Polanyi, *Personal Knowledge* (London: Routledge &
    Kegan Paul, 1958).

21. H. G. Rickover, "A Humanistic Technology," *Nature*, 208, 721
    (1965).

3. FACTS AND REASON IN A NUCLEAR AGE

1. J. K. Galbraith, *The Affluent Society* (London: Hamish Hamilton, 1958).

2. *The Effects of Nuclear Weapons*, ed. Samuel Glasstone (United
   States Atomic Energy Commission, 1962).

3. Giulio Douhet, *The Command of the Air*, trans. D. Ferrari
   (New York: Coward-McCann, 1942).

In *The Command of the Air*, first published in 1921, Douhet, listing his ideas on the nature of air power, considered that the prime purpose of aerial warfare was to obtain command of the air. Having achieved this, air forces could direct their offensive against surface objectives with the intention of crushing the material and moral resistance of the enemy. The maximum returns from such offensives had to be sought beyond the battlefield. It was militarily much more effective to destroy a railway station, a bakery, a power plant, or a supply train than to strafe or bomb a trench.

4. J. Foster Dulles, Address to Council of Foreign Relations (January 12, 1954).

5. Winston S. Churchill, See Hansard, March, 1955, cols. 1899, 1900.

6. For an interesting analysis of the "incident," see Albert and Roberta Wohlstetter's "Controlling the Risks in Cuba," *Adelphi Papers*, No. 17 (London: Institute for Strategic Studies, 1965).

7. Herman Kahn, *On Thermonuclear War* (London: Oxford University Press, 1960). *Thinking About the Unthinkable* (London: Weidenfeld and Nicolson, 1962). *On Escalation: Metaphors and Scenarios* (London: Pall Mall Press, 1965).
Thomas C. Schelling, *The Strategy of Conflict* (Cambridge, Mass.: Harvard University Press, 1960).

8. A recent book by Anatol Rapoport entitled *Strategy and Conscience* (New York: Harper & Row, 1964) levels a number of criticisms against this kind of writing. In a powerful counterattack D. G. Brennan, in the *Bulletin of the Atomic Scientists* (21, p. 25) refers to what he regards as Rapoport's misunderstandings and misrepresentations of the work of the "strategic community" (*sic*), and in particular of Herman Kahn, one of the foremost members of the "community." One passage from this review is worth quoting. "It is certainly true," writes Brennan, "that strategists often analyze some component situation—say a hypothetical missile duel—in terms of abstract opponents A and B." But it is not true, as Rapoport charges, that the strategists do not share "a passionate concern for human values." This statement is justified by the remarkable observation that

"Herman Kahn has often mentioned that Munich was a severe traumatic experience for him, although he was young, only sixteen, at the time." One can comment only by saying that one way or the other, most Europeans also found it a traumatic experience, and that, unlike Mr. Kahn, who was only twenty-two years of age at its end, most also experienced the ravages of war.

9. See, for example, Jerome B. Wiesner and Herbert E. York "National Security and the Nuclear Test Ban," *Scientific American*, 211 (4), 27 (1964).

10. Michel Rouzé, *Robert Oppenheimer, The Man and His Theories*, trans. Patrick Evans (New York: Fawcett World Library, 1965).

11. S. Zuckerman, "Judgment and Control in Modern Warfare," *Foreign Affairs*, 40, 196 (1962).

12. The bearing of this conclusion on the concept of a major conventional war between the Western and Soviet blocs is a matter which calls for separate analysis.

13. *Op. cit.*

14. William C. Foster, "New Directions in Arms Control and Disarmament," *Foreign Affairs*, 43, 587 (1965).

4. THROUGH THE CRYSTAL BALL

1. See J. B. S. Haldane in *Man and His Future* (London: Churchill, 1963).
"Thirty years ago responsible statisticians were writing about 'The twilight of parenthood,' 'Les berceaux vides,' and so on; and I was fool enough to believe them."

2. *Royal Commission on Population Report* (H.M.S.O., 1949), cmd. 7695.

3. *Congressional Hearings on Nuclear Propulsion for Naval Surface Vessels*, October 30, 31, November 13, 1963 (U.S. Government Printing Office, 1964).

4. H. G. Rickover, "A Humanistic Technology," *Nature*, 208, 721 (1965).

5. Presidential memorandum on "Strengthening Academic Capability for Science Throughout the Country" (The White House, Washington, D.C., September 13, 1965).

6. I. I. Rabi, Unpublished address to S.H.A.P.E. (1965).

7. *Statistical Yearbook, 1964* (United Nations).

8. *The State of Food and Agriculture 1964*, F.A.O (H.M.S.O.: 1965).
See also "Food: The Looming Crisis," *New Scientist*, 28, p. 77 (October 14, 1965); and "Future of Food," *New Scientist*, 28, p. 559 (November 25, 1965).

9. See *Man and His Future*, ed. Gordon Wolstenholme (London: Churchill, 1963).

10. Frederick Harbison and Charles A. Meyers, *Education, Manpower and Economic Growth* (New York: McGraw-Hill, 1964).

11. Edgar Snow, "The Chinese Equation," *The Sunday Times Weekly Review* (January 23, 1966).

5. PRIORITIES AND SECRECY IN SCIENCE

1. Christopher Wren, *Parentalia, or Memoirs of the Family of the Wrens* (London: 1750).

2. D. S. L. Cardswell, *The Organisation of Science in England* (London: Heinemann, 1957).

3. Arthur Koestler, *Encounter*, Vol. 25, p. 32 (1965).

4. Stephen Toulmin, "The Complexity of Scientific Choice II: Culture, Overheads or Tertiary Industry?" *Minerva*, IV, 155 (1966).
Basic Research and National Goals: A Report to the Committee on Science and Astronautics, U.S. House of Representatives, by the National Academy of Sciences (Washington: U.S. Government Printing Office, 1965).

5. Margaret Gowing, *Britain and Atomic Energy 1939–1945* (London: Macmillan, 1964).

6. Theodore Fox, *Crisis in Communication* (London: Athlone Press, 1965).

7. Fritz Machlup, "Why Economists Disagree," *Proc. Amer. Philos. Soc.*, 109, 1 (1965).

8. Jerome Wiesner, *Where Science and Politics Meet* (New York: McGraw-Hill, 1965).

6. LIBERTY IN THE AGE OF SCIENCE

1. George Gissing, *The Private Papers of Henry Ryecroft* (London: Archibald Constable, 1903).
   Mabel Collins Donnelly, *George Gissing, Grave Comedian* (Harvard University Press, 1954).

2. A. J. P. Taylor, "London Diary," *New Statesman* (London, November 2, 1958).

3. J. B. Priestley, "Who Goes Where?" *New Statesman* (London, September 6, 1958).

4. Antoine Nicholas de Condorcet, *The Progress of the Human Mind*, trans. June Barraclough (New York: Noonday Press, 1955).

5. Dwight Eisenhower, Speech at Symposium on Basic Research (New York, 1959).

6. Isaiah Berlin, *Two Concepts of Liberty* (Oxford University Press, 1959).

7. Saint-Simon, quoted from Mortimer Adler's *The Idea of Freedom* (New York: Doubleday, 1958).

8. This was written three years before the international agreement to ban atmospheric tests of nuclear weapons.

9. Alexis de Tocqueville, *Democracy in America*, Henry Reeve text revised by Francis Bowen (New York: Knopf, 1946).

10. Aldous Huxley, *Brave New World Revisited* (New York: Harper & Row, 1959).

7. THE SOCIAL FUNCTION OF SCIENCE

1. J. D. Bernal, *The Social Function of Science* (London: Routledge, 1939).

2. J. G. Crowther, *The Social Relations of Science* (London: Macmillan, 1941).

3. John R. Baker, *The Scientific Life* (London: Allen & Unwin, 1942). *Science and the Planned State* (London: Allen & Unwin, 1945).

4. Michael Polanyi, *The Logic of Liberty* (Chicago University Press, 1951).

5. John R. Baker, *The Scientific Life* (London: Allen & Unwin, 1942).
   "Men who like administration think that it is good for the populace to be treated like a herd of sheep. Nowadays there are those who think it good not only for the populace but also for scientific research workers. This is the message of Bernal's *Social Function of Science.*"

6. *Science in War* (London: Allen Lane [Penguin Special], 1941).

7. C. P. Snow, *The Two Cultures and the Scientific Revolution*, Rede Lectures (Cambridge University Press, 1959).

8. See *Report of the Committee on the Management and Control of Research and Development* (London: H.M.S.O., 1961).

9. Michael Polanyi, *Personal Knowledge* (London: Routledge & Kegan Paul, 1958).

10. In the introduction to the official record (London: H.M.S.O., 1963) of "The Origins and Development of Operational Research in the Royal Air Force" there is a reference to a "manifesto" on operational research, then a new term, which was published by a small group of scientists, among whose number I found my own name. The manifesto referred to turned out to be *Science in War*, which was published anonymously in August, 1940.

11. See note 6.

12. It has changed even further since this was written. For an up-to-date record of our present organization, see *The Promotion of the Sciences in Britain* (Central Office of Information, 1965).

13. Hansard. November 9, 1960, col. 406.

14. J. K. Galbraith, *The Affluent Society* (London: Hamish Hamilton, 1958).

15. See note 12.

16. "Science and Society" (1960). An essay issued by Associated Electrical Industries to mark the Tercentenary of the Royal Society.

17. C. H. Waddington, *The Ethical Animal* (London: Allen & Unwin, 1960).

18. Since I made this observation in 1960, a variety of conflicting views on the subject have appeared, partly because of the increasing growth of the resources that have gone to science and technology in all countries, and partly because of the fact that the term "science policy" has achieved a respectable status, with annual or biannual international ministerial meetings on the subject under the auspices of the European Organization for Economic Cooperation and Development. On one side we have men like Maurice Goldsmith, who in a piece in the London *Times* of January 12, 1966, entitled "Bringing Science under Control," declares that "as the resources of men and money devoted to science are becoming significant in volume, it is essential for countries to form a "science policy," which may be defined as a deliberate attempt by governments to make the most of the total science effort of the nation"—although he admits that we are colossally ignorant about how one does it. In order to increase the area of enlightenment, he has helped form a "Science of Science Foundation," whose "First Annual Lecture" was delivered recently by Professor Derek J. de Solla Price of Yale University under the title, "The Scientific Foundation of Science Policy" (*Nature*, 206, 233, April 17, 1965). Price's general theme is that if we can learn why science works as it does, and how it reacts with society, we might discover a key which leads us to "a more efficient science policy."

On the other side we have men like Alvin M. Weinberg, Director of the Oak Ridge National Laboratory of the United States Atomic Energy Commission, who while recognizing, as we all do, the importance of the establishment of national policies for science in countries which are backward (for example, see George V. Haniotis on "The Search for a National Scientific Policy in Greece" in *Minerva*, III, 312), is more concerned, as I am, with the basic problem of scientific choice.

In a series of articles published in *Minerva,* which is a review of science, learning and policy (Vol. I, 1963, pp. 159–71, Vol. II, 1964, pp. 3–14 and Vol. IV, 1965, pp. 3–4) he makes much the same general point that I was concerned to bring out in my 1959 and 1960 addresses (Chapters 6 and 7 of this volume). In his most recent article he speaks about the "planning reports" which have been produced, under the auspices of the Committee on Science and Public Policy of the U.S. National Academy of Sciences, by specialist groups representing different branches of science, but points out that in indicating their achievements and promise they all tend to be "isomorphic." He then goes on to say:

> It makes little difference whether the field is astronomy, physics, or computers: its achievements have been outstanding, its promise superb and its needs and tastes very expensive. Nor is this surprising. Each report is prepared by dedicated members of a particular scientific community whose passions and aspirations, as well as knowledge, center on a single field. The very reasonable theory underlying the preparation of these reports is that each field should put its very best foot forward. Judgments among the fields would then be made by a higher body, like the President's Science Advisory Committee, that represents many different scientific fields.
>
> Actually, the political process out of which flows our ordering of priorities does not work that neatly. Though the Science Adviser carries great weight, Congress and the separate government agencies must also be reckoned with and their views are harder to bring into focus. Interpretative and philosophic analysis of the problem of scientific choice, particularly judgments as to relative priority, will therefore remain important. Such judgments, by the nature of things, can hardly be other than individual opinions. Out of such individual views and opinions is fashioned a climate of thinking, an intellectual environment, which impinges in countless small ways on those in Congress and in the agencies who make scientific policy.

In a further passage in the same piece Weinberg goes on to say:

> Any judgment as to the relative worth of any field of human activity involves an assessment of how that activity bears on human values. In particular, we support large-scale science because, in one way or another, we believe that out of large-scale

science will come human benefits or values. Now the *value* of science cannot be determined from within science. It is a venerable philosophic principle that the value of any universe of discourse must be judged from outside that universe of discourse.

It was for this reason that in his first article in *Minerva*, on "Criteria for Scientific Choice," Weinberg urged "that large-scale public support be given a field of science *only if* it rated well with respect to what I called 'external criteria.'" These he identified "as technological merit (meaning bearing on related technology), scientific merit (meaning bearing on related fields of science) and social merit (including national prestige, culture, etc.)."

19. In the final and Seventeenth Annual Report of the British Government's Advisory Council on Scientific Policy, which was set up in 1947 and which gave way to a new set of official advisory committees in 1965, the Council, with which I had been closely associated from its formation, wrote:

The main issue, and the most enduring issue, which has exercised the Council during its seventeen years of existence has been the question of the scale and balance of our national civil scientific effort. We cannot pretend to have done more than achieve a measure of the magnitude of the problem, and of the great responsibilities which would rest on those who, unlike ourselves, might one day be charged with the task of cutting up the cake of our national scientific resources.

We have had to form judgments about the scale of the scientific effort of other leading nations. The importance of this task has increased progressively both with the widening realization that the success of our whole economy depends on the wise exploitation of modern science and technology, and with an increasing awareness of the fact that a major reason for our deteriorating position in world markets is the success with which other countries have exploited their own scientific efforts. We have had to compare the scale of our efforts in technology and applied science with that in fundamental research; we have considered the balance of effort between the various sciences, and in some scientific fields, of the relationship of our national to our international efforts. Matters such as these, and the emergence of vastly expensive areas of scientific activity—for example, nuclear physics, oceanography, and space technology—were the major reason why it became necessary to devise a new machinery for reviewing civil scientific requirements as a whole.

It is interesting to record that when the Advisory Council came into existence, the government was spending on civil science, so far as can be estimated, less than a tenth of the resources that are made available today. Given the demands of which we are already aware, the figure could easily double in the next five years. This level of expenditure may well prove necessary if we are to continue to compete successfully in those fields of science in which we are now operating. Expenditure on this scale would enable our scientists, now being turned out at five times the rate they were when we began our work, fully to deploy their abilities, and to build the essential background to our technological effort in industry, as well as to provide the trained manpower which industry requires if it is to prevail against the ever-increasing strength of overseas competition.

On the other hand, Britain clearly cannot engage freely in certain extensive fields of science, such as space technology or high-energy physics, if this would involve restraining the growth of other potentially fruitful fields of knowledge. This means that priorities in science will have to be determined. We ourselves have never had the powers to tackle this problem, even if we had had the kind of foresight without which any statement of priorities could prove a highly dangerous exercise. We know of no way to determine precisely what proportion of any country's gross national product should be devoted to the advancement and exploitation of science. Our own view is that the United Kingdom is still spending too little. But, if the resources which the government can set aside for science cannot be increased sufficiently to allow us to embark on all the good scientific projects of which we know, it will be up to government itself to decide, on the best advice that can be tendered, what our national priorities should be.

This is the most important issue which we pass on to our successors. The problem of priorities in science and technology lies at the heart of national science policy, and therefore of our national destiny.

20. University College, University of London, under whose auspices the Rickman Godlee lecture was delivered.

21. Charles Goodeve, "Science and Social Organization," *Nature*, 188, 180 (1960).

22. My Rickman Godlee lecture was delivered the day after the election of the late President Kennedy. The results of the poll were not certain at the time I spoke.

23. See note 9.

24. It has been much changed even in the past year. See note 12.

25. This was written in 1960. The first astronaut went into orbit on April 12, 1961.

26. J. G. Crowther, *Founders of British Science* (London: Cresset Press, 1960).